Workbook

for

Levin and Fox

Elementary Statistics
in Social Research

Ninth Edition

prepared by

David R. Forde
University of Memphis

Boston   New York   San Francisco
Mexico City   Montreal   Toronto   London   Madrid   Munich   Paris
Hong Kong   Singapore   Tokyo   Cape Town   Sydney

To obtain permission(s) to use material from this work, please submit a written request to Allyn and Bacon, Permissions Department, 75 Arlington Street, Boston, MA 02116 or fax your request to 617-848-7320.

ISBN 0-205-37780-7

Printed in the United States of America

10 9 8 7 6 5 4 3 2 1   08 07 06 05 04 03 02

TABLE OF CONTENTS

PREFACE

This workbook includes a series of exercises that is designed to complement topics covered in Levin and Fox's *Elementary Statistics in Social Research*, 9th Edition.   Their textbook emphasizes theoretical issues, shows how to complete hand computation of statistics, and demonstrates applications of statistics. This workbook emphasizes using a computer to obtain the information and the "interpretation" and "presentation" of results of statistical analysis.

The material in the workbook includes:
- Computer lab activities with problems and solutions in each chapter
- Basic computer commands for the Statistical Package for the Social Sciences (SPSS © Student Version 10.0 and Full Version 11.0)
- Instructional codebooks
- Instructions for using James Alan Fox's *Statistics Calculator*
- A brief introduction to *ContentSelect*
- Exercises and work-sheets in each chapter

Additional materials and software for the exercises in this workbook requires:
- Access to SPSS software. SPSS software is available as 1) full version, 2) graduate package, and 3) studentware. For the full version, many Universities and Colleges provide access to site-licensed use of the full version in their computer labs.   Some students may wish to purchase the "Graduate Pak" which includes the base and professional statistics options.   Other students wishing to work on their own computers may purchase SPSS studentware which allows users to work with smaller datasets (50 variables and 1500 cases).
- Obtaining a copy of the instructional data sets from the web-site (see information about downloading on page iii of this preface);
- Microsoft Excel© in order to use Fox's *Statistics Calculator*

STATISTICS IN SOCIAL SCIENCES

Working with statistics in the social sciences can be both interesting and informative. I'd like to ask you a few questions before we start:

1. How many murders were there last year in the United States?

   (Your answer) _____

2. What is the population of the United States and what percentage of it is Black?

   (Your answers) _____; _____

For some reason, most Americans fear numbers. John Allen Paulos (1990) in *Innumeracy: Mathematical Illiteracy and Its Consequences* wrote about how most people will not tolerate illiteracy yet they will neglect to learn about numbers making incredible bungles.

Vandiver and Giacopassi (1997) report that most students don't have a good grasp of crime numbers as they greatly overestimate the extent of crime. Sigelman and Niemi (2001) explain how both Whites and Blacks overestimate the size of the Black population by staggering amounts. Compare your guesses to the information that follows.

In 2000, there were about 15,517 murders (including non-negligent manslaughter). You can obtain yearly estimates on homicide from the Federal Bureau of Investigation in their annual report on *Crime in the United States: Uniform Crime Reports.* It is also available on-line at www.fbi.gov in the link to the UCR.

The United States Bureau of the Census reports that the population of the USA on April 1, 2000 was about 281 million people and that about 12.3 percent were Black or African American. It can be accessed on-line at www.census.gov.

How close were your guesses? What factors might explain why some people make guesses that are far away from the actual numbers? Are these "official" statistics about homicide and population as provided by governmental agencies even accurate? Wow! These are hard questions to answer.

If we as a society really want to tackle social problems such as crime, poverty, racial inequality, and other issues, we are going to need to work to obtain a basic grasp of statistics. My challenge to you is to go through the exercises in this book thinking about how the numbers work and how you can best present the information so that a non-statistician will understand what you have done.

Let's go get the data files and get started with these exercises.

WEB-SITE FOR DATASETS

The instructional SPSS datasets are located on the Allyn and Bacon Web-site as a supplement to Levin and Fox's textbook. You will need to have internet access using a browser such as Internet Explorer. Type the link address into the address line in the browser as:

www.ablongman.com/levinstats9e/

If this link does not work, go to the main page of www.ablongman.com. Search for Jack Levin and then follow the links.

Additional instructions will be provided on the web-page, but the basics are:

- Get a 1.44 floppy diskette (or zip-disk)
- Go to the web-site and click on the links to save the files to diskette

There are three SPSS files to download:

- mtf90_00.sav – A subset of variables from the 1990 and 2000 Monitoring the Future Study

- noscj95.sav – A subset of variables from the 1995 National Opinion Survey of Crime and Justice

- gss98.sav – A subset of variables from the 1998 General Social Survey

JAMES ALAN FOX'S STATISTICS CALCULATOR

James Alan Fox has developed a statistics calculator for Levin and Fox's 9th Edition of Elementary Statistics in Social Research. This calculator is available as a file for download from the Allyn and Bacon web-site. You must have Microsoft Excel© to use this calculator. The file is quite large at about 5.6 MB. I recommend that you download it on to a zip disk. Once you have the file and you are working on a computer that has Excel, click on the file to start the calculator. The main menu is shown below.

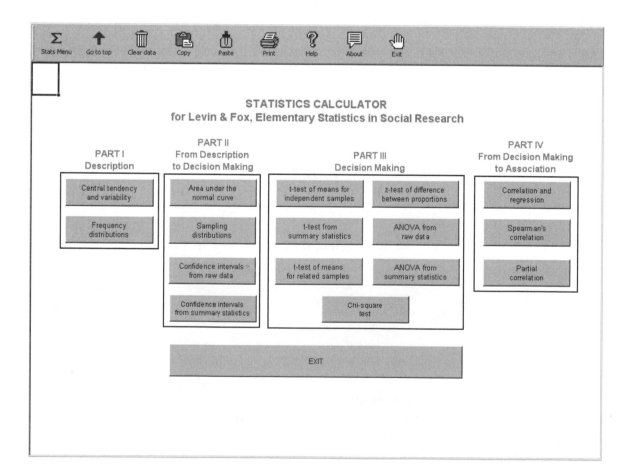

This statistics calculator is very easy to use. It calculates statistics as you enter data into a spreadsheet. You will see examples of how to use it in later chapters. It is an excellent tool for small data sets where you are entering the data directly into the program.

CONTENT SELECT

Whether you are writing a paper that is reviewing literature or writing about your own research project, it is important that you are able to find research articles, to understand them, to summarize their findings, and that you compare them to your own research. Keep track of where you find things. Accurate and complete citations are important for documenting the source of information. A research methods class will focus on how the information was sampled. In this workbook, we will focus on how to develop an effective summary of statistical information.

ContentSelect is an on-line collection of leading scholarly and peer-reviewed journals in Sociology, Psychology, Criminal Justice, and many more areas. *ContentSelect* is bundled with some textbooks. *ContentSelect* is a powerful tool that allows students to use keywords to search for articles. It allows downloading of abstracts, reading of full text of articles, e-mailing of searches, and downloading of Adobe Acrobat files (original format) of many articles.

A button link to *ContentSelect* is on the Allyn and Bacon web-site. Below, I have logged on to the website and checked the box for *ContentSelect* Sociology.

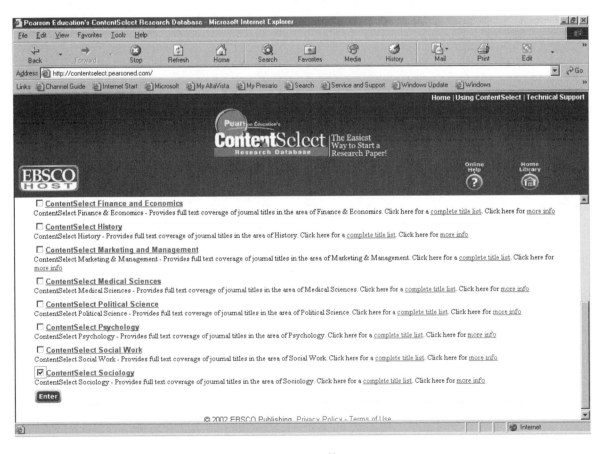

If you do not have access to *ContentSelect*, you should learn how to access on-line periodical search engines in your college or university library system (e.g. Sociofile, PsychLit, etc.) and paper abstracting sources such as Sociological Abstracts or Psychological Abstracts.

In this example, I would like to search for research articles on "abortion." Keywords and phrases can be used. Type the keyword into the box and click on "Search."

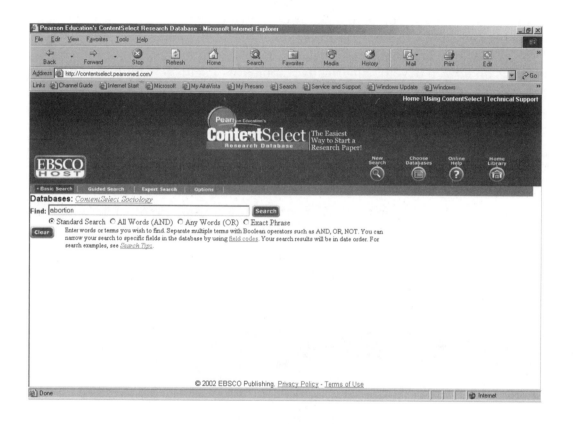

The results of the search are shown on the next page. You will get these and new articles if you try this same search. These data bases are updated regularly. There are 59 articles available for viewing. You may wish to add additional terms to focus upon a more specific issue when you find a very large number of articles for your topic.

It is a good idea to read the abstracts to learn more about an article. To do this, click on the title of the article. I selected article number 8 in this list. The abstract is shown on the next page. At this point, I could read the full text by clicking on the link at the bottom of this screen. I could also e-mail the results of the search to my account.
An e-mail of abstracts and sources will help you to document your search and to keep an accurate list of references for your research.

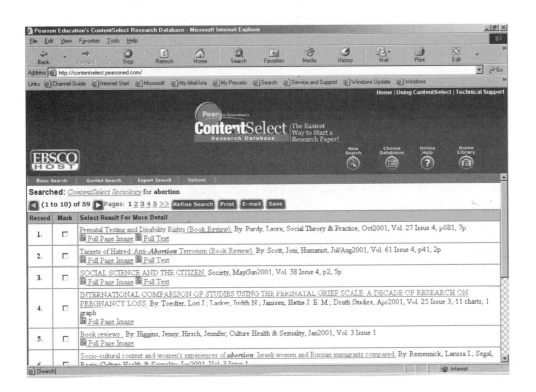

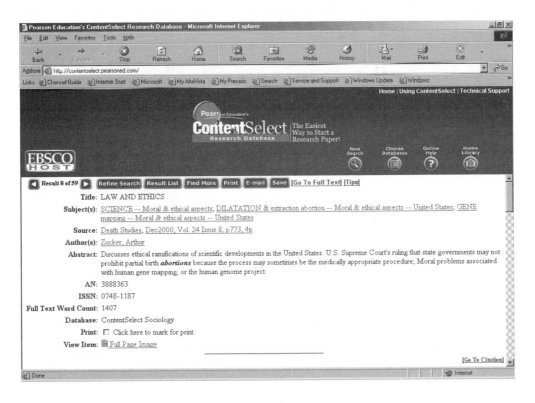

Additional Readings

American Psychological Association (2001). *Publication Manual of the American Psychological Association.* Washington, DC: APA

    The APA manual is used by many social science journals as a referencing tool. It provides guidelines on organizing papers, presenting statistical information, and citation of references.

Huff, D.H. (1993). *How to Lie with Statistics.* W.W. Norton and Company.

    This classic is a small book first published in 1954. Huff shows how numbers can be used to oversimplify, bamboozle, confuse, and terrorize the general public. I strongly recommend it.

Paulos, J.A. (1990). *Innumeracy: Mathematical Illiteracy and Its Consequences.* Vintage Books.

    Paulos provides a wake-up call to America in which he coins the term innumeracy as analogous to illiteracy.

Sigelman, L., & Niemi, R.G. (2001). Innumeracy about minority populations: African Americans and Whites compared. *Public Opinion Quarterly, 65,* 86-94.

    Sigelman and Niemi discuss how Americans distort estimates of minority populations. They suggest that people's own experiences (e.g. living in an area with high or low minority populations) influence estimates.

Vandiver, M., & Giacopassi, D. (1997). One Million and Counting: Students' Estimates of the Annual Number of Homicides in the U.S. *Journal of Criminal Justice Education*, 8, 135-143.

    Vandiver and Giacopassi report how students overestimate the murder rate and they discuss some reasons why this may happen.

Acknowledgements

I would like to thank Lance Roberts and Mike Gillespie who "bothered me" a whole lot when I had to learn statistics. Any errors in this workbook though are mine.

STATISTICAL ANALYSIS: READY OR NOT, LET'S GO!

INTRODUCTION

Chapter1 is designed to ease you into analyzing data sets by introducing the Statistical Package for Social Sciences (SPSS ©), codebooks, and some descriptive statistics. These data sets will be analyzed using SPSS for Windows. It assumes that you have obtained the instructional datasets. If you have not, please read the web-site section in the preface to this workbook.

In this chapter you will see that statistical analysis looks complex on a first attempt, but that it is quite easy to complete if you proceed systematically, identify basic assumptions about variables, choose a statistical procedure, generate the computer output, and then interpret it. Just keep in mind that you will be building a repertoire of analytic skills as you complete each chapter.

CODEBOOKS

The data sets used in these exercises are drawn from publicly available data library files of the Inter-university Consortium for Political and Social Research (ICPSR). Three different studies are used:

1. The Monitoring the Future Study (Appendix A);
2. The National Opinion Survey of Crime and Justice (Appendix B); and
3. The General Social Survey (Appendix C).

You will need to read the codebooks to learn the format and placement of the data. Read the preface and introduction of each codebook for a brief explanation of these data. We will use a small subset of questions excerpted from each of these studies. These data sets and questions from each were selected because they cover a broad range of issues in the social sciences.

Codebooks are important because they tell us about the kinds of information that are stored in a data set. We will want to know about variables and their attributes. In order to do this using SPSS, we will need to know a variable's acronym, and how its attributes are coded. Different researchers may use different methods of coding information and you, as a researcher, will need to read the codebook in order to understand how a data set is put together.

Let's start by looking at the codebook from the National Opinion Survey of Crime and Justice. Flip to Appendix B. You'll see a brief description of when and how the data set was collected. Notice that this codebook looks a like a questionnaire with introductions to each section. We are going to want to identify the following:

- Variable acronyms (or mneumonics)
- Variable labels
- Value labels (Coding categories)
- Missing values

The first section of the questionnaire asks about the presentation of crime in the media. The researchers who made this codebook have numbered questions as "Letter" followed by a number. Figure 1 highlights the key components of question M2.

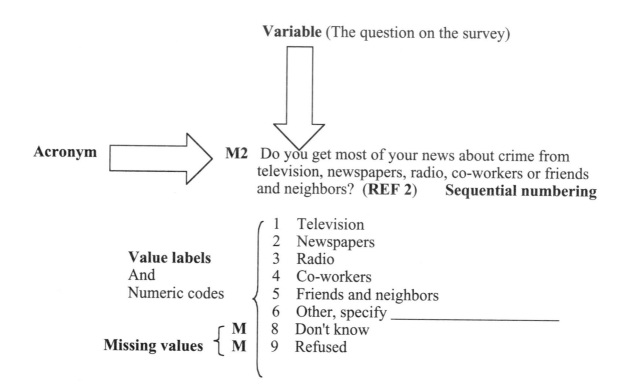

Variable (The question on the survey)

Acronym   **M2** Do you get most of your news about crime from television, newspapers, radio, co-workers or friends and neighbors? **(REF 2)**   **Sequential numbering**

Value labels
And
Numeric codes

	1	Television
	2	Newspapers
	3	Radio
	4	Co-workers
	5	Friends and neighbors
	6	Other, specify _____
Missing values { **M**	8	Don't know
M	9	Refused

Figure 1 Breaking down the key components of a variable in a codebook

Looking at Figure 1, the variable acronym for this question is M2. It is important to know this fact because "M2" is used to identify the variable in the SPSS file. Take a moment to identify other variable acronyms in the codebook. I have also added a reference number to each variable in this codebook to provide a sequential location of the variables. Soon you will see that SPSS can locate variable based on an alphabetical listing of acronyms or by their sequential ordering within the data file.

This variable "M2" represents information about peoples' primary source of information about crime. This codebook provides the exact wording of the question and how responses were recorded for each variable. In most instances, this codebook it is quite clear in identifying the topic of study. In the future, as you read other codebooks, you will see that the NOSCJ is an example of a "very good" codebook. Looking now at Figure 2, note that the variable M2 is labeled by these researchers as "Where get news about crime."

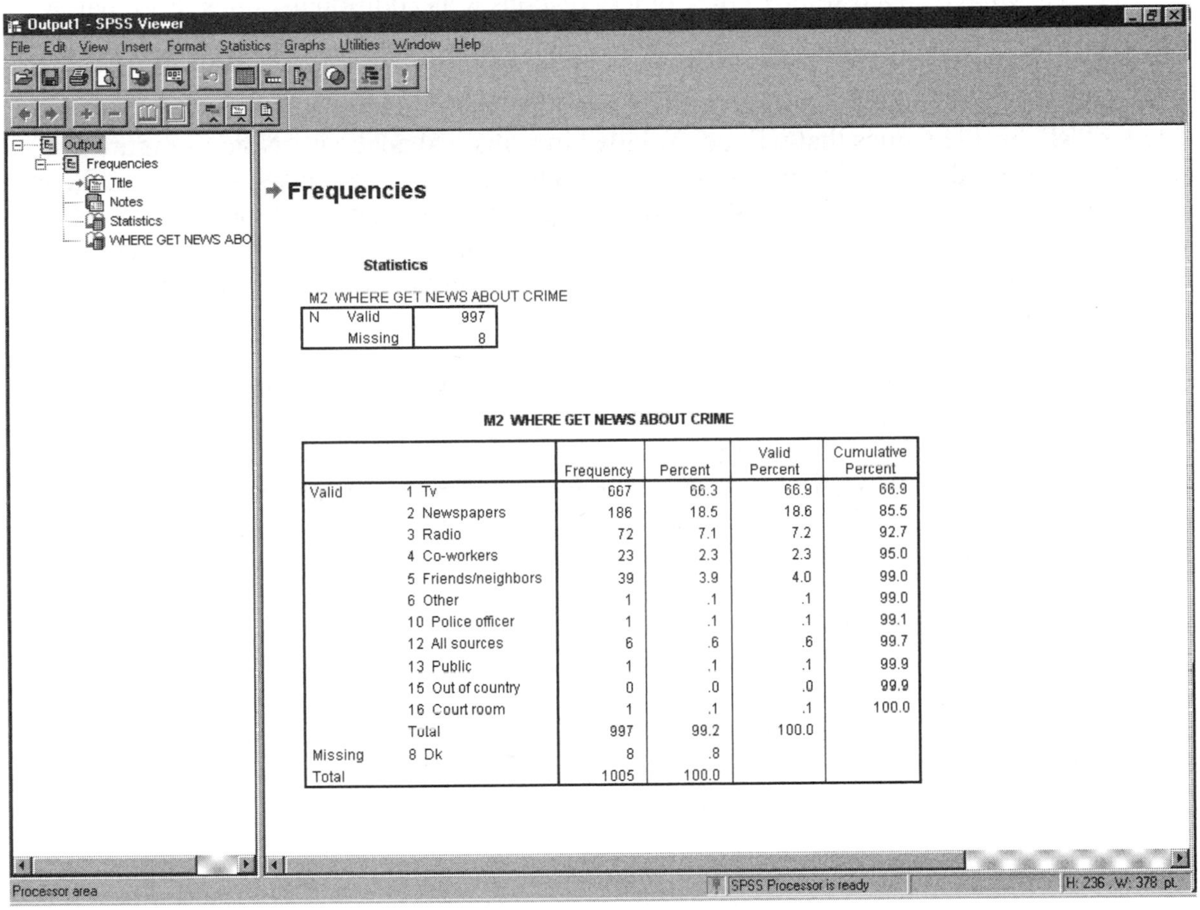

Statistics

M2 WHERE GET NEWS ABOUT CRIME

N	Valid	997
	Missing	8

M2 WHERE GET NEWS ABOUT CRIME

		Frequency	Percent	Valid Percent	Cumulative Percent
Valid	1 Tv	667	66.3	66.9	66.9
	2 Newspapers	186	18.5	18.6	85.5
	3 Radio	72	7.1	7.2	92.7
	4 Co-workers	23	2.3	2.3	95.0
	5 Friends/neighbors	39	3.9	4.0	99.0
	6 Other	1	.1	.1	99.0
	10 Police officer	1	.1	.1	99.1
	12 All sources	6	.6	.6	99.7
	13 Public	1	.1	.1	99.9
	15 Out of country	0	.0	.0	99.9
	16 Court room	1	.1	.1	100.0
	Total	997	99.2	100.0	
Missing	8 Dk	8	.8		
Total		1005	100.0		

Figure 2 SPSS Output showing the frequency distribution for variable M2

A good variable label should be descriptive. You will see several instances in the Monitoring the Future Study (MTF) where you will have to go to its codebook in order to decipher the question that was asked. While the MTF is a fabulous study, the researchers have used many abbreviations which are not intuitive and sometimes are indecipherable (at least, to my weak eyes). It is a good practice to try to make labels that describe the variable, and to always go back to the codebook to ensure that you have a clear understanding of what the variable is designed to measure.

Next, let's go back to Figure 1 and say that you were asked where you get most of your information about crime. Suppose you say that you get it from a friend. Here the coding category for your answer is friends and neighbors and the numeric code is a "5." I, on the other hand, say that I get my information from a police officer. Where would this go? Looking at Figure 1, we would say that this goes as other - specify, or a "6." Move to Figure 2 and note the codes 10, 12, 13, 15, and 16. What has happened here? Unfortunately, the researchers did not provide the reader with a complete summary of the variable and value labels that have used in their dataset. They have coded some of the "other" responses as additional values. Fortunately, this does not happen too often but it serves to show that you must carefully read codebooks.

A final part in reading a question in a codebook is "missing values." These are denoted by the letter "**M**" beside values that will be excluded in statistical analysis. Note in Figure 1.1 that there are M's beside Don't know, and Refused. When doing our analysis, we would like to know how many people answer the question (valid responses) and how many people did not answer it (missing responses). Look at Figure 1 now and you'll see that information that is missing is reported at the bottom of the table. There were eight people (0.8 percent) who did not answer this question.

Learning to read a codebook is an important part of data analysis. You will need to know where variables are located in a dataset, how things are labeled, and whether there are any missing values for a variable. Note also that this codebook presents the questions on the survey in the order that the questions were asked. Another codebook may present questions in alphanumeric sequence (A's, B's, C's, etc.; or as var1, var2, var3, etc.). It is very important to read the codebook to learn how the data set was put together.

LEVELS OF MEASUREMENT

Variables may be characterized on many dimensions. It is important to understand the properties of variables because the types of analysis a researcher may do depends on how a variable is measured and treated. This workbook provides a brief introduction to four traditional levels of measurement.

Levels of measurement

Level	Properties				Codebook
Nominal	difference				D16
Ordinal	difference	rank			N8
Interval	difference	rank	equidistant		D13
Ratio	difference	rank	equidistant	zero	D14

4

Nominal measures simply imply a difference in categories of a variable. While a number is assigned to each category there is no inherent meaning beyond a difference in the categories. Examples of nominal measurement include sex and race. Sex is a variable with two categories (dichotomous): male and female. Race, in this dataset, is a variable with four categories: white, hispanic, african-american, and others. The numbers assigned to each category are referred to as codes rather than values since they (the numbers) have no meaning. For example, in coding race, each category is coded as a number from 1 to 4 but no order is implied in assigning a number.

Ordinal measures classify a difference and rank order categories. They do not tell us how much of a difference there is between cases or the difference between a case and a real zero. They simply compare a category with other categories (or a set of categories) of a variable. They do not have a standardized metric.

Interval measures classify differences, rank, and imply equidistance between categories. Interval measures rely on a metric or standard unit of measurement. These are sometimes called scales or scalar measures.

Ratio measures are the highest level. They have all of the properties of each of the other types of variables: differences, rank, equidistance between values of categories, plus a real zero. For example, age in years can be considered as a ratio variable with zero being birth and each unit representing one year of time. Note that Levin and Fox combined ratio with interval measures. In practice, the same statistic is used for both interval and ratio level variables. It is important that you, as a researcher, are able to recognize the properties of variables. In each of the labs you will be asked to consider the level of measurement and whether a metric is **discrete** or **continuous**. These decisions will influence how you may interpret statistical analysis of a metric. For example, in interpreting age as a continuous variable you would then assume that values between integers are valid (e.g 13.4 years is a valid possibility between 13 and 14). Lastly, you must consider whether the variable is treated as **dependent** or **independent**. Treatment of variables as dependent or independent will allow you to examine one or more variables as the cause of another which is a theoretical issue, not a statistical issue. For example, sex, race, and family characteristics are variables that generally are treated as independent variables while others are examined as dependent variables.

Note, while you will be asked to identify each of the levels of measurement, you should also be aware that ordinal variables are the most difficult to work with statistically. There are two methods to get around problems with ordinal variables. First, one can treat an ordinal variable as if it is nominal and proceed with nominal level statistics; or, second, more commonly one can treat the categories as if they are interval assuming that values represent a common metric. There are advanced statistics to test the validity of an ordinal to interval assumption, but they are rarely tested. As "statisticians" we are going to want to work with statistics that will help us to best understand the relationship between variables. In some chapters, we will need to disclose our "assumptions" about using an ordinal level as an interval level measure because interval level variables allow greater flexibility in analysis than others.

GET THE DATA FILE USING SPSS

There are several ways to retrieve a data file in SPSS. A dialogue box, shown below, comes up when SPSS is started. By default, it asks whether you wish to "Open an existing data source." We do, so click on OK at the bottom of the screen.

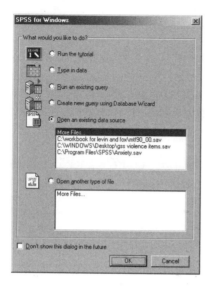

On the next screen, change the "Look in" location to where you have the dataset. In this case, it is on the Floppy A: drive. SPSS by default shows SPSS system files of type (*.sav). To retrieve the datafile, double-click on the filename. When successful, the data file will come up as variables in the SPSS data editor. If you do not see the spss data file listed in this window, check that your diskette is inserted into the drive, check the correct drive is listed (A, B, or perhaps a zip drive D or F). You'll need to specify the correct drive for your computer.

DATA ANALYSIS

The main objective of Chapter 1 is to produce a *frequency distribution* for each variable. The frequencies procedure in SPSS can be located using the drop down boxes by clicking on ANALYZE, then DESCRIPTIVE STATISTICS, and finally FREQUENCIES. The drop down box on my computer is shown below. I have set the options so that variable names (rather than labels) are shown in the order that they appear in the data file. Other people may prefer labels and alphabetical listings of acronyms.

You may change these settings (and you may really want to do so!!) by clicking on EDIT and Options. You'll need to do this each time you have a session on a lab computer. You'll only need to do it once if it is on your own computer. I also have changed the output labels to "names and labels" and "values and labels." Make these changes, close SPSS, and restart it.

Changing the options will make it easier for you to read output and to locate variables within a data file. Try it and you'll see that it isn't too complicated. You can also proceed without making these changes.

The FREQUENCIES procedure in SPSS gives the number of times (frequency) for each value (or code) of a variable. This is reported as a proportion where the number of occurrences is divided by the total number of cases. Percentages are proportions multiplied by 100. Valid percentages are what we are most interested in where these represent the number of cases when a valid response was given.

Researchers will begin their data analysis by looking at frequencies to see the distribution of values on a variable. Is a particular value common or rare? Do people in America favor or oppose the death penalty for persons convicted of murder? You can answer this question by knowing the distribution of cases on the variable. In later exercises, you will also learn that knowing the frequency distribution will assist you in deciding whether or not a comparisons between values are possible (A rule of thumb is that of 100 cases there should be 20 in a group/category for reliable comparisons to be made; there should be at least 20 percent in a group/category).

DATA ANALYSIS EXAMPLE

Research Problem: Are there enough blacks and whites in the National Opinion Survey of Crime and Justice sample to permit racial comparisons in statistical analysis? Open the SPSS data file: **noscj95.sav**. Find **D2** in the variable list. It is listed near the end of the data file. Click on D2 and it will move to the right side of the box. Click on OK and it will generate a frequency distribution for race (D2). Provide an interpretation of the results in which you describe the variable, its level of measurement, the results of the study, and the source of your information.

Computer output: Different computer programs generate different types of output. The objective of these lab exercises is not to show you a specific type of computer output but instead to have what kinds of things you should look for in computer output. In fact, most computer programs may generate different forms of output so that the same program may provide different things for one user versus another. A sample format of computer generated output is shown for D2. The frequency distribution shows the variable that was analyzed, the value and label for categories, and statistical information. We are most interested in the number of valid cases, and the valid percentages. If you edit the output options, your output will look like the frequency distribution shown below

D2 RACIAL/ETHNIC GROUP

			Frequency	Percent	Valid Percen	Cumulative Percent
Valid	1	Anglo	817	81.3	81.9	81.9
	2	Hispanic	77	7.7	7.7	89.6
	3	African	77	7.7	7.7	97.3
	4	Other	3	.3	.3	97.6
	10	Am.indian	12	1.2	1.2	98.8
	14	Asian	12	1.2	1.2	100.0
		Total	998	99.3	100.0	
Missing	9	Rf	7	.7		
Total			1005	100.0		

Interpretation: Write a short summary of what you've found. A detailed summary for this variable follows:

The National Opinion Survey of Crime and Justice conducted in 1995 surveyed 1005 Americans about a variety of crime and justice issues. The survey also included a demographic question about the race of the respondent. Race (D2), in this study, is measured as a nominal level variable with four major categories. A frequency distribution shows that about 82% of the respondents were White (Anglo), 8% were Black (or African-American), 8% were Hispanic, and about 3% were other races. Only about 1% of respondents failed to answer this question. Their answers are excluded from statistical analysis. Since there are substantially fewer Blacks, Hispanics, and Other races than Whites in this sample [less than a nominal 20 percent cut-off point] we will not permit statistical comparisons between races using these data. [Note, these percentages are approximately the same as the actual percentages in the American population].

Note that there is a lot of information to include in every interpretation of statistical results. A brief checklist for a good interpretation is that it will report:
- the source of information;
- level of measurement;
- valid percentages;
- total "N" for a study;
- missing data
- and, an interesting aspect of a variable.

KEY TERMS

Acronym
Codebook
Dependent variable
Frequencies
Levels of Measurement
      Nominal
      Ordinal
      Interval
      Ratio
Independent variable
Missing values
SPSS
Variable label
Value label

Name _____   Date _____

Complete the following problems.
Detach the sheets to hand them in (as requested)

CHAPTER 1 PROBLEMS

Tasks/Interpretation: Fill in the blank for each variable.

1.   You will need to become comfortable with the measurement properties of the variables. Complete the information for each variable referring to the codebook as necessary. You must determine the level of measurement for each variable. **This task can and should be completed before you go to a computer lab.**

2.   Generate a frequency distribution for each variable. Do them ONE (or a few at a time) to speed the analysis.

3.   For each variable, write a short explanation which answers the research problem (below). Your interpretation should answer the issues from the checklist (source, level of measurement, suitability of variable, valid percentages, missing data, and an interesting aspect of the data). Write your interpretations in the space that is provided.

4.   Familiarize yourself with the codebooks. You will be using them in all of the statistical exercises.

I recommend that you proceed systematically for one research problem before going on to the next one. Read the questions, use the computer, and write an interpretation before moving to the next problem.

*Research Problem*s; Use the National Opinion Survey of Crime and Justice, 1995 to find:

1.   What percentage of the sample is female?   Are percentages in this sample large enough that we can compare males to females?

Name _____   **Date** _____

2.   What percentage of the sample has a household income over $60,000? Find the variable
        name. Are the percentages in each group large enough to make comparisons across
        groups?

For the following variables, generate a frequency distribution and describe an aspect of the data
that is of interest to you.

3.   Regular viewer of TV programs such as COPS, America's Most Wanted, etc.

4. What percentage of Americans says that they feel safe in their neighborhood (N10)?

Name _____ **Date** _____

Use the Monitoring The Future study to analyze the following.

5. What percentage of high school students has ever smoked marijuana (or hashish)?

6. How often in the (past 12 months) have high school students had to visit a doctor because of injuries suffered in a fight, assault, or auto accident?

7. Select a variable of interest to you. Report on an aspect of it.

Name _____   Date _____

Use the General Social Survey to analyze the following:

8. Analyze the GSS questions on abortion: ABANY, ABRAPE, and ABSINGLE. What are the percentages of Americans that say "yes" it should be possible for a woman to obtain a legal abortion for each of these situations?

9. What is your opinion on these same questions about abortion?

10. What do you think may explain why some people may say yes or no to these questions?

11. Use ContentSelect to find two articles about attitudes toward abortion. Try to identify the theories that the author(s) use to explain people's attitudes? On a separate sheet, write a two-page summary of your findings.

BUILDING A DATA FILE

INTRODUCTION

This chapter provides an introduction to the structure of data sets. It describes some of the common procedures used to create data sets using SPSS. It demonstrates how to label variables and their attributes, and discusses the importance of labeling variables and documentation of data sets. Lastly, the Inter-university Consortium for Political and Social Research (ICPSR) is introduced.

STANDARD DATA STRUCTURE

There are a wide variety of statistical analysis programs that may be used to analyze data. If you've used a computer, you may already have used a spreadsheet program such as Microsoft Excel, Microsoft Works, or Lotus-notes to balance your checkbook. These spreadsheets enable users to perform mathematical manipulations (e.g. add or subtract) down columns and across rows. Spreadsheets, however, are typically limited in the number of variables that may be included and in the ease to which statistics may be computed. People seeking to do statistical analysis more often will go to a "canned" program that is designed for computing statistics.

Two of the most readily available statistical programs are the Statistical Package for the Social Sciences (SPSS), and Statistical Analysis Systems (SAS). Both of these packages are widely used by Universities, Government, and Businesses. These programs are available for use on different kinds of computers ranging from mainframes, to local area networks, to personal computers (e.g. Windows 2000 and MacIntosh).

Social scientists typically work with very large data sets. A mainframe application is used by the US Government to analyze the hundreds of variables and millions of cases in the US Census of Population. With the increased speed and power of personal computers (PC) it is now possible to analyze the National Crime Survey on a PC even though this is still a very large data set with hundreds of variables and about 60 thousand cases. The student version of SPSS is limited to fifty variables (50) and fifteen hundred cases, but its set-up and manipulation of data sets follows the same principles as the full SPSS package.

The standard format of a data set is such that columns of a data matrix represent variables. Each variable in SPSS has an acronym (up to eight characters) such as var1, var2, var3, et cetera. Each variable may include two or more categories with assigned values. If you are collecting your own data you will make the decisions about how to operationalize each variable. If you are using a data set that was collected by someone else, then you will need to read their codebook to understand the representation of **variables** and **values**.

Box 1 Data Matrix of Variables (columns) and Cases (rows)

ID	VAR1	VAR2	VAR3	VAR4	VAR5	Etc.
1	90	1	16	1	1	
2	90	2	15	1	1	
...	90	2	14	3	1	
2000	90	2	17	3	1	

Box 1 shows a data matrix. The **columns** in the matrix represent **variables**. Variables are the record of what the researcher has measured in his or her study. For example, a variable may be the information about a person's response to a question on a survey. Or, a variable may be more computed by combining information from several variables in a data set to form an index (We will recode variables and compute an index in Chapter 6). The **rows** of a data matrix represent **cases**. Each row contains the information about variables for a particular case. In the example above, we can see that there is an identification variable (ID) and that case number 1 has values of 90 on variable 1, 1 on variable 2, 16 on variable 3, and so on. The numbers in a data matrix become informative once we know what the variables and cases represent.

There are several ways to create a data matrix in SPSS. The data can be entered directly into the data editor, it can be read in as in-line data as "syntax," or it can be entered into a spreadsheet and imported. We'll do each of these using a very small amount of data.

Let's make up some hypothetical data for an example with six people answering a survey about their fear of crime. This question on fear of crime has been included on several National Crime Surveys asking people "How safe do you (or would you) feel when walking alone at night in your own neighborhood?" Responses to the question are very safe (4), safe (3), unsafe (2), very unsafe (1), and no response (0). We'll also record whether the person is male (M) or female (F). And, we will assign an identification number to each case. The data: Case one is a male who feels safe; case two is a female who feels unsafe; case three is a female who feels safe; case four is a male who feels very safe; case five is a female who feels very unsafe, and case six is a male who refused to tell us how he felt. We will enter this information into a data matrix.

Now, let's go ahead and start the SPSS for Windows program. I will use the Student version in this example. In Windows 95/98/2000, click on the start button, move up to Programs, and down to the SPSS 10.0 for Windows Student Version icon. A successful start will take you to the default pop-up window asking you "What would you like to do?" This window is shown in Figure 1.

Click in the circle for "Type in data" and then click on "OK." A new or untitled SPSS data file will be created. The variable names and case numbers are blank.

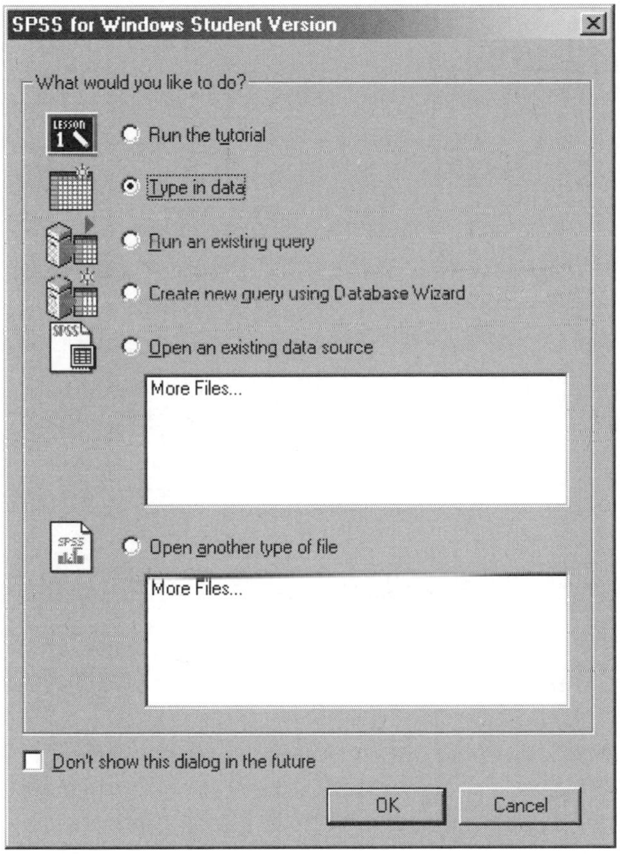

Figure 1 Start-up window for SPSS Student Version 10.0

In SPSS 10 and 11, there are "Data view" and "Variable view" tabs at the bottom of the data editor screen. We're going to create two variables and enter some data for each. We will need to define the variables, designate a format, and then label everything! To begin, click on the variable view tab and type "gender" into the top left cell. Figure 2 shows the "variable view" dialogue box.

Untitled - SPSS Data Editor										

File Edit View Data Transform Analyze Graphs Utilities Window Help

	Name	Type	Width	Decimals	Label	Values	Missing	Columns	Align	Measure
1	gender	Numeric	8	2		None	None	8	Right	Scale
2										
3										
4										
5										
6										
7										
8										
9										
10										
11										
12										
13										
14										
15										
16										
17										
18										
19										
20										
21										
22										
23										
24										
25										
26										
27										
28										
29										
30										
31										
32										

Data View **Variable View**

SPSS Processor is ready

Figure 2 Variable view dialogue box

Note that we will need to set the options on all aspects of variables. Right now, gender is set at the default settings with no labels and a numeric size of 8 wide and 2 decimal places with no labels, no missing values, and so on. Let's change each option to something that is appropriate.

In Chapter 1 we looked at levels of measurement. Note that some of the levels of measurement are shown in Figure 2 as scale, ordinal, and nominal. A user may designate for SPSS procedures the level of measurement of a variable. If you do this, SPSS will attempt to assist you in selecting appropriate statistics. More often, though, most users will not take the time to complete this step. Next, there are several very important settings in this dialogue box: type, labels, and missing values.

There are many types of formats of variables. The most common formats are numeric and string. The numeric form is defined using a fortran code of x.y with x being the number of figures and y being the number of decimal places. The default format for numeric data in SPSS is 8.2. Let's look at our example. How many possibilities are there for gender? That is, how wide can the variable be? 1-9 is a width of 1, 10-99 is 2, 100- 999 is 3, and so on. Are there any decimal places for gender? No. We'll want to change the TYPE to 1 wide with 0 decimal places. Click on "Type" and do this now.

A second common type of variable is so-called "string" format. String variables are alphanumeric (letters and/or numbers) that may range from 1 to 255 characters. A string format is usually used when letters are an efficient way of operationalizing categories. Examples include the common operationalization of gender as M and F, to typing in of the open-ended responses to a question on a survey, to recording the exact spelling of names of people. For gender, we'd can operationalize male and female as M and F because people easily recognize the categories. For open-ended questions, we'd like an interviewer or data entry person to type the response to the question. My experience with string variables is that they will work for open-ended questions when the response is expected to be relatively short. That is, the response can be typed in 20 to 40 character spaces. If string variables are very long, over the years, it has been my experience that string variables are generally difficult to analyze, or worse yet that they hinder analysis. As such, I try to use numeric variables avoiding string variables when a numeric code can be used. The primary reason for using numeric format is that there are instances where the same variable (e.g. gender) operationalized as a numeric variable can be used in statistical analyses but the string variable cannot be included.

Labeling of variables and their attributes is an important part of data entry. Labels should be **descriptive** and there should be a label for **every attribute** including missing values. The only exception to this rule is that on scales we may want to just label the minimum and maximum values (e.g. Very satisfied [1] to very dissatisfied [7] with intermediate values blank [2 to 6]). Try to avoid the use of abbreviations and acronyms because you may forget what they stand for and they make it difficult for other people to read your work. People do use acronyms in codebooks but they should be avoided. You will see many acronyms in the Monitoring the Future data set that is included with this workbook. In some cases, their use of acronyms is clear and in others it is very difficult to interpret the computer output without going to their codebook. The major goal in using labels is to make the computer output readable for you and for others.

There are two kinds of labels to add to a variable: variable and value labels. Labels should provide a description of the basic content of the variable. Look at figure 2 to find LABEL. For our example, let's label fear as "Feel safe walking at night." Next we need to add labels for Each of the values/categories. Click on values and three dots will appear. Double click on these dots to bring up the "value labels" dialogue box. These are entered one at a time by entering the value, the label, and then clicking on "add." Every possible value including no response (0) should be labeled. Once everything has been entered you will click on continue. These procedures are repeated for every variable.

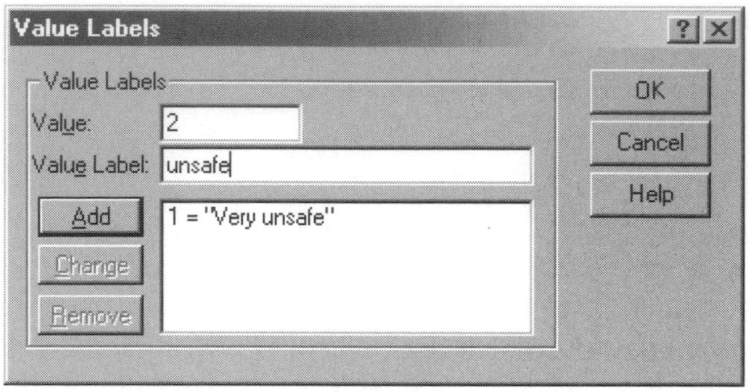

Figure 3 Value Labels dialogue box

The third major feature in defining data is that values of variables may be set as **valid** or **missing**. Statistical analyses will count the number of **valid cases** for a variable. For example, people may refuse to answer a question, or they may not know, or a question may be not applicable. The researcher will want to know the average for people who answered the question, and to know the number of missing cases in his or her statistical analysis. The statistical software must be instructed which responses are to be treated as **missing values**. This is done by clicking on the MISSING tab in the variable view (Figure 2). Missing values may be assigned as specific numbers or as a range of numbers.

A good codebook will inform the user about the assignment of all codes and it will provide information about missing values. For example, in Box 2, D16 is the variable name for sex of the respondent in the National Opinion Survey of Crime and Justice. Find this question in the codebook. Note that the variable is labeled as "Sex of the respondent." Each of the coding categories 1, 2, and 0 are labeled, in turn, as male, female, and unknown. And, lastly there is an "M" beside the 0 indicating that 0s are set as missing values and excluded from statistical analysis

Box 2 Example of valid and missing values from the codebook for the National Opinion Survey of Crime and Justice:

D16	Sex of the respondent	
	1	Male
	2	Female
	M 0	Unknown

Figure 4 shows how to define missing values for our variable fear. We want to set zero as a discrete missing value.

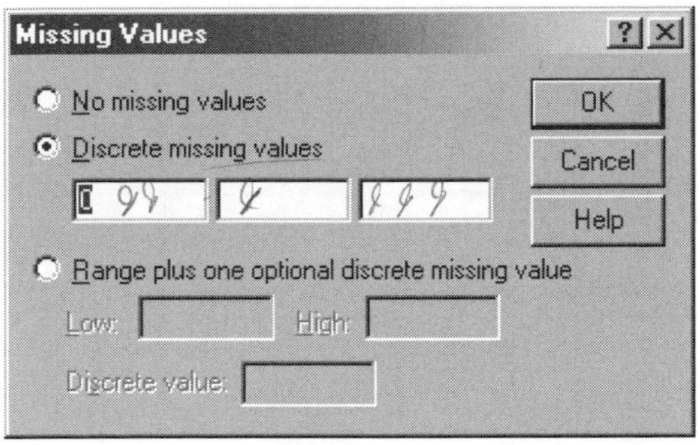

Figure 4   Missing Values

Missing values are set by the researcher. You must look to see whether particular values are excluded or should be excluded from statistical analysis of data. Do not assume that these are set properly when you use a data set that has been put together by someone else. In fact, most researchers will turn all missing values off when they archive their data because different statistical packages may treat missing values in different ways. It is up to you as a researcher to ensure that these are set properly.

By now you can see that we have all of the necessary information for defining each of the three variables for our exercise. Try it yourself by creating the variables, adding labels, setting missing values, and then entering all of the data for the six people. When you are complete the data editor should look like the data editor shown in figure 5. Where necessary, you can adjust the width of columns to see variable names by clicking and dragging the border between variables.

For our example, let's assume that we will code gender as male= 1, and female =. Fear will be coded as Very unsafe =1, unsafe = 2, safe = 3, very safe = 4, and no response = 0. The six people for this exercise are:

male and safe	1, 3
female and unsafe	2, 2
female and safe	2, 3
male and very safe	1, 4
female and very unsafe	2, 1
male and no response	1, 0

Enter these data into SPSS and your screen should look like figure 5.

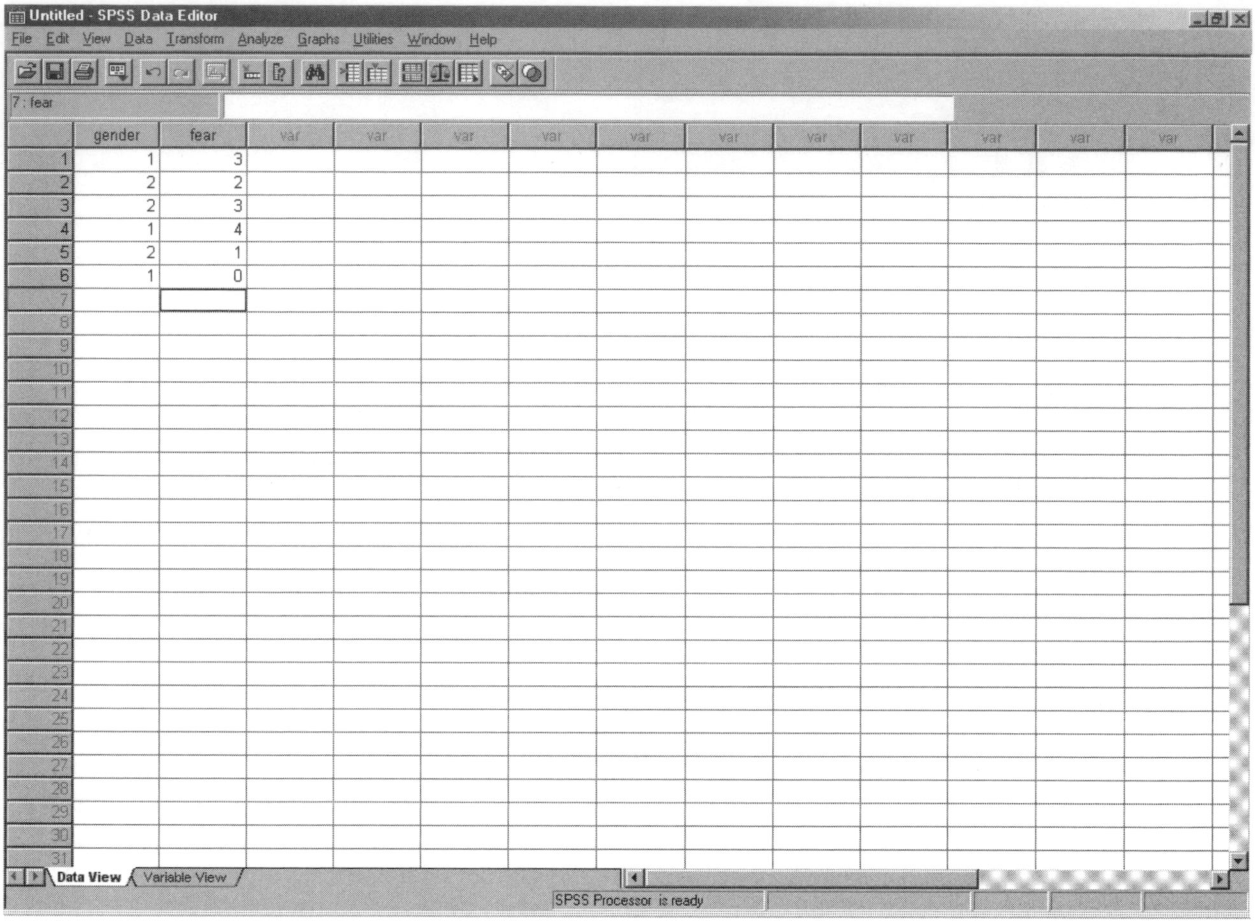

Figure 5 Completed data matrix for example on fear of crime

The real test to see how well you've entered the data and its associated information comes when you produce a frequencies distribution. There should be **labels on everything** and **missing values should be active**. Generate frequency distributions for gender and fear using the same procedures that you used in Chapter 1: Analyze, Descriptive Statistics, Frequencies ....

Figure 6 shows the computer output.

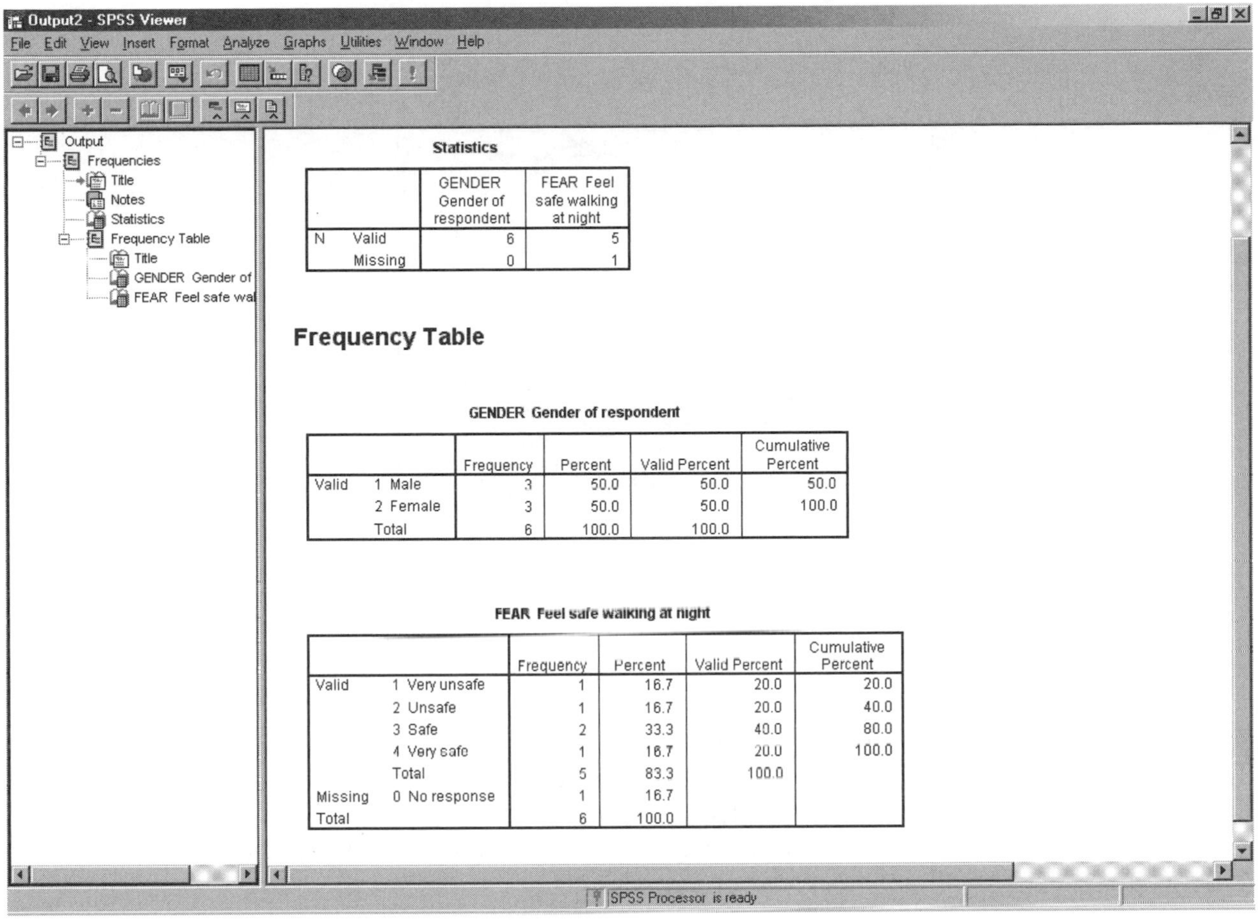
Output2 - SPSS Viewer
File Edit View Insert Format Analyze Graphs Utilities Window Help
Output
Frequencies
Title
Notes
Statistics
Frequency Table
Title
GENDER Gender of
FEAR Feel safe wal
SPSS Processor is ready

Statistics

		GENDER Gender of respondent	FEAR Feel safe walking at night
N	Valid	6	5
	Missing	0	1

Frequency Table

GENDER Gender of respondent

		Frequency	Percent	Valid Percent	Cumulative Percent
Valid	1 Male	3	50.0	50.0	50.0
	2 Female	3	50.0	50.0	100.0
	Total	6	100.0	100.0	

FEAR Feel safe walking at night

		Frequency	Percent	Valid Percent	Cumulative Percent
Valid	1 Very unsafe	1	16.7	20.0	20.0
	2 Unsafe	1	16.7	20.0	40.0
	3 Safe	2	33.3	40.0	80.0
	4 Very safe	1	16.7	20.0	100.0
	Total	5	83.3	100.0	
Missing	0 No response	1	16.7		
Total		6	100.0		

Figure 6 Frequency distributions for gender and fear

These frequency distributions are "clean" with labels on each of the variables and values. A good starting point in any analysis is to look at frequency distributions to ensure that there are no "wildcodes." Wildcodes may be data entry errors where an incorrect value was entered into the computer, or they may be values where a label is needed. It is a normal part of data entry to examine computer output, and to fix these problems.

Putting together a data set can be a lot of work. Thus, you may want to save your data file. This is done from the data editor window by clicking on file, and then save. Figure 7 shows the save data dialogue box.

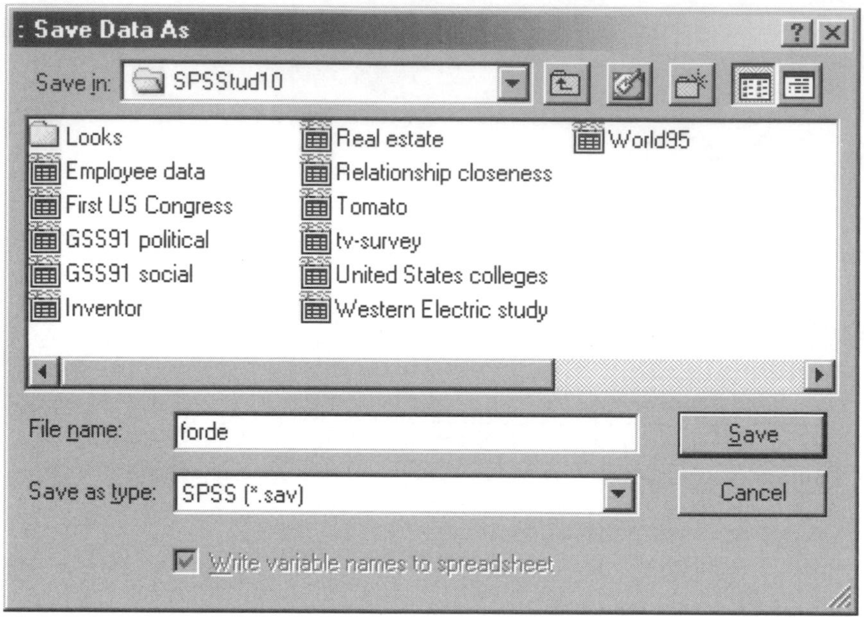

Figure 7 Saving data

The default folder for SPSS student version is a folder called "student." The default type of file is an SPSS file. You may type in any name. I have typed my last name since that is what I ask students to do when handing in a completed data file. I have many students and if their name is on it, I know that it is their data file. The file may also be saved on a diskette by changing the save in folder from student to a floppy disk drive (A:).

At this point, you have seen all of the necessary steps to create and save an SPSS data file. In the next section, you will see how larger datasets are created and accessed using a syntax window. Information is also provided about the Inter-University Consortium for Political and Social Research.

SPSS Syntax

The SPSS Base manual describes SPSS syntax in much greater detail. These manuals can be purchased from SPSS. While they are moderately expensive, they are useful. Also, these manuals are often available in a reference section of university libraries and/or reference areas in large computer rooms.

What I would like you to see in this example is that there are several key elements in the syntax file that you also create for the same data set when you use the data editor. The data list statement defines the format of variables. The variable and value labels statements add appropriate labels. A missing values statement sets missing values for fear. The begin data and end data statements are used with in-line data. Each statement is ended by a period which tells SPSS to move to the next command. SPSS calls this period a "command terminator."

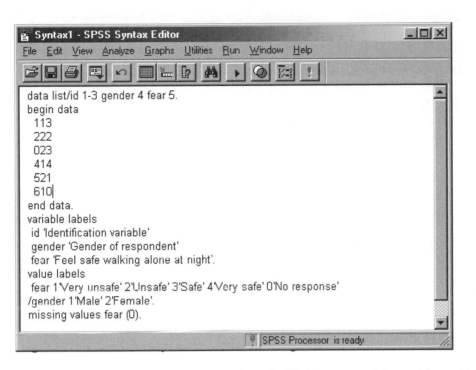

Note that SPSS Studentwarecannot handle SPSS syntax. You will need to use the full version if you wish to try using the syntax window for this exercise. The importance of knowing about SPSS syntax is that it is used to activate many of the large data sets that are archived by the Inter-university Consortium for Political and Social Research (ICPSR). SPSS syntax statements can be read by most versions of SPSS software, and each version has used the same basic syntax.

DATA LIBRARIES

Another important source of data files is the Inter-University Consortium for Political and Social Research (ICPSR). Many federally funded projects have a requirement that the data from the project be archived in a format that can be accessed by other people. ICPSR data librarians have taken peoples' data sets and saved the raw data, SPSS syntax, and/or SAS syntax. Their hard work means that you have access to many data sets in the ICPSR data library. If you are considering a term paper, thesis, or advanced research project you may want to access a data file from the ICPSR library.

Importantly, you now know that someone had to spend the time to enter these data, add variable and value labels, and set missing values. It is still quite a bit of work to prepare a data set from a data library, but it is a valuable resource potentially saving you the time that it took to collect the original data, and the cost is low (in fact FREE to most users).

Figure 9 shows the entrance window to the National Archive of Criminal Justice Data. This is a topical archive at the Inter-universityConsortium of Political and Social Researchwhich is located at the University of Michigan in Ann Arbor, Michigan. You can access it on the world wide web at: www.icpsr.umich.edu. The National Archive of Criminal Justice Data is one of the topical archives at ICPSR.

Figure 9 The National Archive of Criminal Justice Data

Click on download data (on the left side of the screen) to go to a search screen where you can browse the site for different types of data sets, and eventually request to download the data file

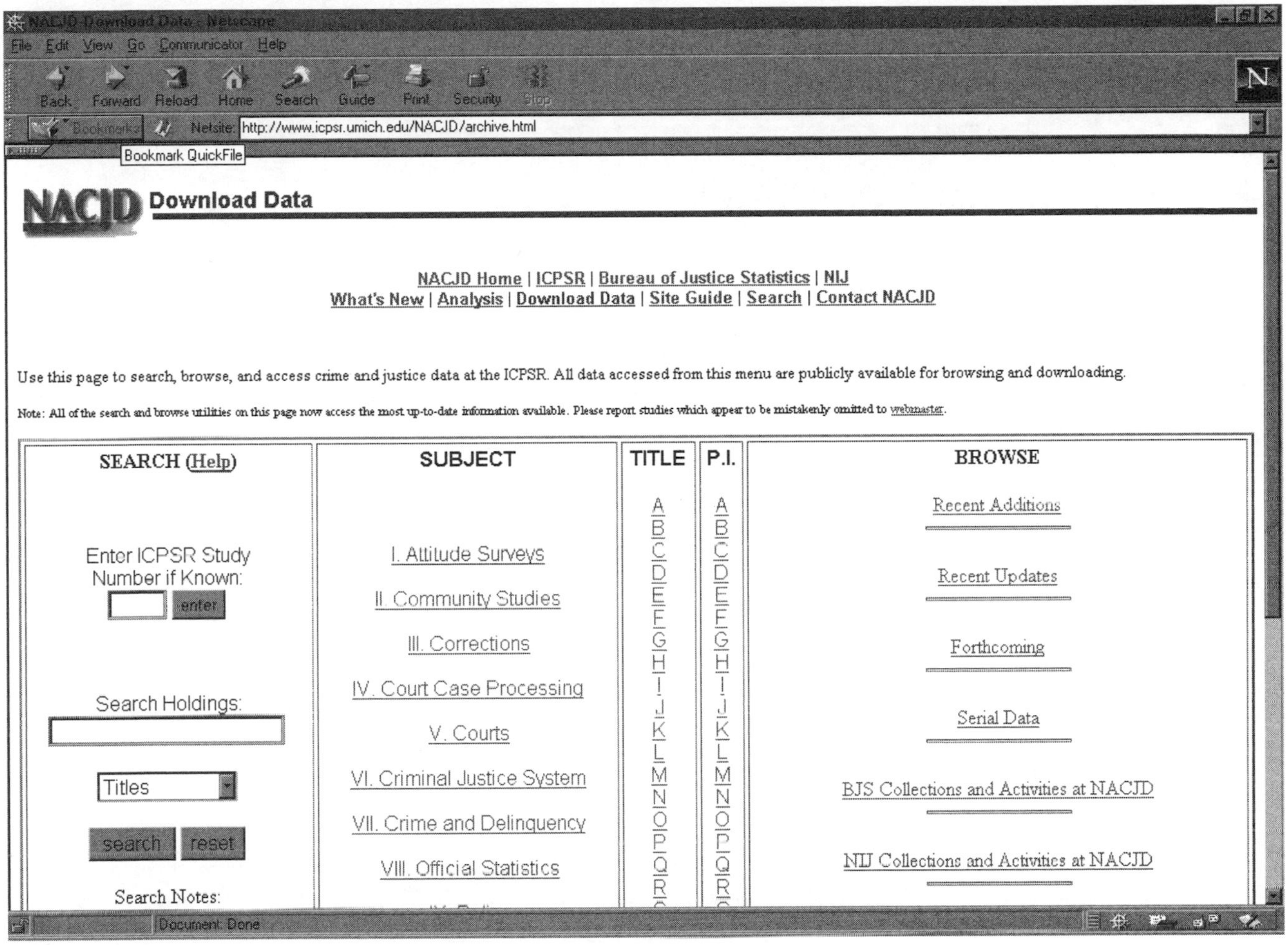

Figure 10 Download screen at NACJD

Figure 10 shows the subject listing of topics in the National Archive of Criminal Justice Data. We would like to locate the National Opinion Survey of Crime and Justice that is included with this workbook. We could enter the ICPSR study number because it is shown on the first page of the codebook for the study (6720). Let's find it under the subject listing which includes attitude surveys. To begin, click on "Attitude Surveys."

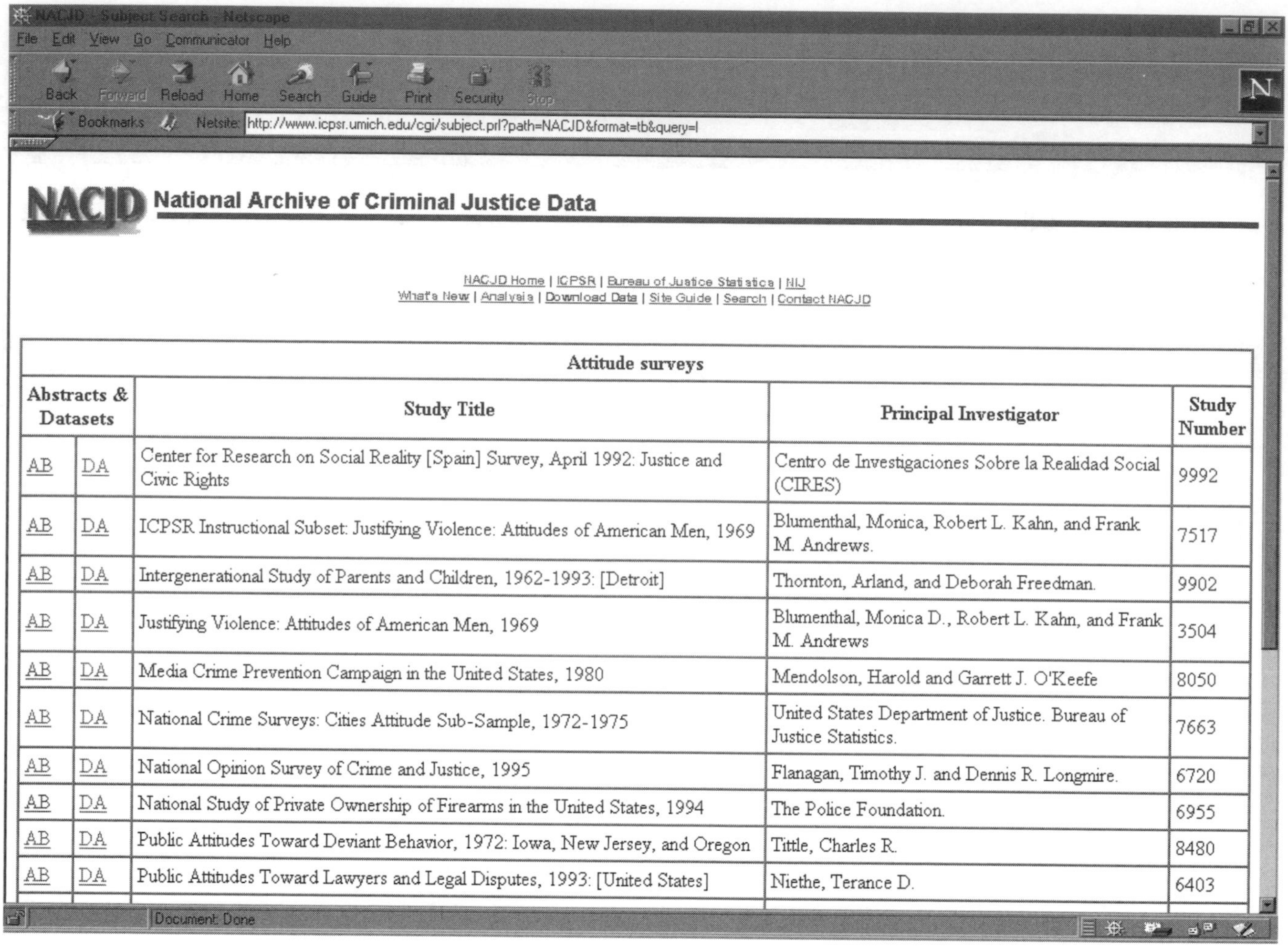
NACJD National Archive of Criminal Justice Data

NACJD Home | ICPSR | Bureau of Justice Statistics | NIJ
What's New | Analysis | Download Data | Site Guide | Search | Contact NACJD

Attitude surveys				
Abstracts & Datasets		Study Title	Principal Investigator	Study Number
AB	DA	Center for Research on Social Reality [Spain] Survey, April 1992: Justice and Civic Rights	Centro de Investigaciones Sobre la Realidad Social (CIRES)	9992
AB	DA	ICPSR Instructional Subset: Justifying Violence: Attitudes of American Men, 1969	Blumenthal, Monica, Robert L. Kahn, and Frank M. Andrews.	7517
AB	DA	Intergenerational Study of Parents and Children, 1962-1993: [Detroit]	Thornton, Arland, and Deborah Freedman.	9902
AB	DA	Justifying Violence: Attitudes of American Men, 1969	Blumenthal, Monica D., Robert L. Kahn, and Frank M. Andrews	3504
AB	DA	Media Crime Prevention Campaign in the United States, 1980	Mendolson, Harold and Garrett J. O'Keefe	8050
AB	DA	National Crime Surveys: Cities Attitude Sub-Sample, 1972-1975	United States Department of Justice. Bureau of Justice Statistics.	7663
AB	DA	National Opinion Survey of Crime and Justice, 1995	Flanagan, Timothy J. and Dennis R. Longmire.	6720
AB	DA	National Study of Private Ownership of Firearms in the United States, 1994	The Police Foundation.	6955
AB	DA	Public Attitudes Toward Deviant Behavior, 1972: Iowa, New Jersey, and Oregon	Tittle, Charles R.	8480
AB	DA	Public Attitudes Toward Lawyers and Legal Disputes, 1993: [United States]	Niethe, Terance D.	6403

Figure 11 Listing of Attitude Surveys

Notice that the National Opinion Survey of Crime and Justice study is located about two-thirds of the way down this listing of studies. We've found it! Now, we would like to know what the study is about and to find out about the format of the data files. Click on the abstract (AB) for the study. The abstracts tell you a bit about the study, whether there is an on-line codebook, and provides a summary of the structure of the data set(s).

An ICPSR abstract gives a brief description of the purpose of the project. At the end of them, they also provide references where additional published information about the study can be found. Most data sets also have on-line (machine readable) documentation of codebooks and questionnaire instruments (if applicable). This extent of documentation about the collection of data is described under the heading "Extent.collect." The same line also tells you that there are SPSS and SAS data definition statements (syntax). Further down in the abstract, we find the approximate size of the data files. For example, the National Data has 103 variables and 1005 cases. Recall that SPSS Student version can handle 50 variables and 1500 cases. Importantly, the full version of SPSS can easily handle these files. Lastly, note that ICPSR provides a suggestion for citation of these materials.

Box 3 Abstract for Study 6720 (excerpted and italics added)

DATE-UPDATED = Feb. 13, 1997;

INVESTIGATOR = Flanagan, Timothy J., and Dennis R. Longmire.;

TITLE = NATIONAL OPINION SURVEY OF CRIME AND JUSTICE, 1995;

SUMMARY = The purpose of this survey was to provide legislators, public officials, and Texas residents with a reliable source of information about citizens' opinions and attitudes concerning crime and criminal justice related-topics. The data collection consists of two distinctly different files, National Data (Part 2) and Texas Data (Part 1), which can be linked or used separately for analysis. The survey questions concern neighborhood atmosphere and presentation of crime in the media, worries regarding possible attacks--both robbery and physical attacks, confidence in and opinions of police and their effectiveness, problems dealing with courts, and attitudes regarding prisoners and prisons, drug laws and drug problems, and juvenile gangs. Other questions focused on attitudes concerning the death penalty, guns, and the availability of firearms. The National Data file contains additional information expanding on the respondent's sources of crime news and gang-related questions. Demographic information on respondents includes sex, age, race, income, education, and religion.;

EXTENT.COLLECT = *2 data files + machine-readable documentation (text) + SAS data definition statements + SPSS data definition statements + data collection instrument;*

RESTRICTIONS = In order to preserve respondent confidentiality, certain identifying variables are restricted from general dissemination. Aggregations of this information for statistical purposes that preserve the anonymity of individual respondents can be obtained from ICPSR in accordance with existing servicing policies.;

DATA.TYPE = survey data;

EXTENT.PROCESS = DDEF.ICPSR/ MDATA.ICPSR/ REFORM.DOC/ RECODE;

DATA.FORMAT = LRECL with SAS and SPSS data definition statements.;

PARTNO = 1
  PART.NAME = Texas Data
  FILE.STRUCT = rectangular
  CASE.COUNT = 501
  VARIABLE.COUNT = 114

LRECL = 184
RECORDS.PER.CASE = 1

PARTNO = 2
PART.NAME = National Data
FILE.STRUCT = rectangular
CASE.COUNT = 1,005
VARIABLE.COUNT = 103
LRECL = 191
RECORDS.PER.CASE = 1

RELATED.PUBS = Sims, Barbara. "The National Opinion Survey of Crime and Justice, 1995: Development and Methods". In T.J. Flanagan and D.R. Longmire (ed.), AMERICANS VIEW CRIME AND JUSTICE. Thousand Oaks, CA: Sage Publications, forthcoming.;

RELATED.PUBS = Longmire, D.R., and Barbara Sims. "1995 Crime Poll: Texas and the Nation" (Executive Summary). Huntsville, TX: Sam Houston State University, Survey Research Program, Criminal Justice Center, 1995.;

CITATION = Flanagan, Timothy J., and Dennis R. Longmire. NATIONAL OPINION SURVEY OF CRIME AND JUSTICE, 1995. ICPSR version. Huntsville, TX: Sam Houston State University, Criminal Justice Center, Survey Research Program [producer], 1995. Ann Arbor, MI: Inter-university Consortium for Political and Social Research [distributor], 1996.;

KEYWORDS = crime, justice, opinion;

        If you decide that you want a data set and machine readable documentation is not provided, please check with your reference librarian about ordering a paper copy of the code book from ICPSR. Many Universities and Colleges have memberships in ICPSR and students can often obtain a code book for a nominal fee (sometimes free).
        Next, we would like to download the data. Go back to the previous screen and click on DA (see Figure 11). A permissions screen will pop-up (Figure 12). Many ICPSR data sets are available for free to the general public for research purposes. Just enter your e-mail ID and you will move to the next screen. ICPSR may ask you to complete a brief questionnaire asking you who you are, where you are located, and what you plan to do with the data.

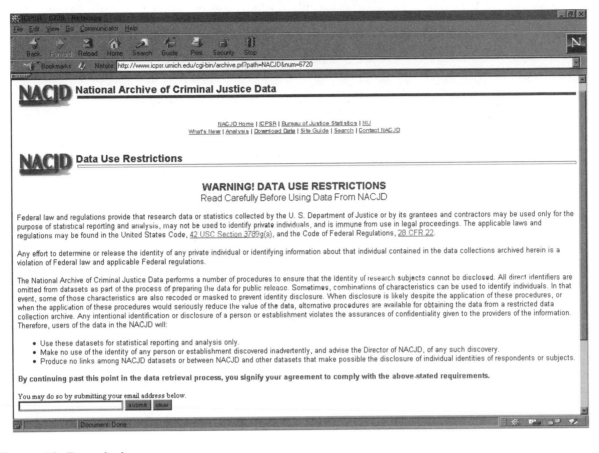

Figure 12 Permissions screen

The final steps to putting together a data set involve selecting the files that you need to download. The main items are documentation (codebook or questionnaires), raw data, and data definition statements (SPSS, SAS, et cetera). Figure 13 shows that there are eight files for study 6702. For this workbook, I downloaded the codebook for the National data, the data itself, and the SPSS statements. I selected the compressed files and decompressed them using a zip utility. The uncompressed files can also be selected, but this may be very slow if you have selected a large data file such as the National Crime Survey.

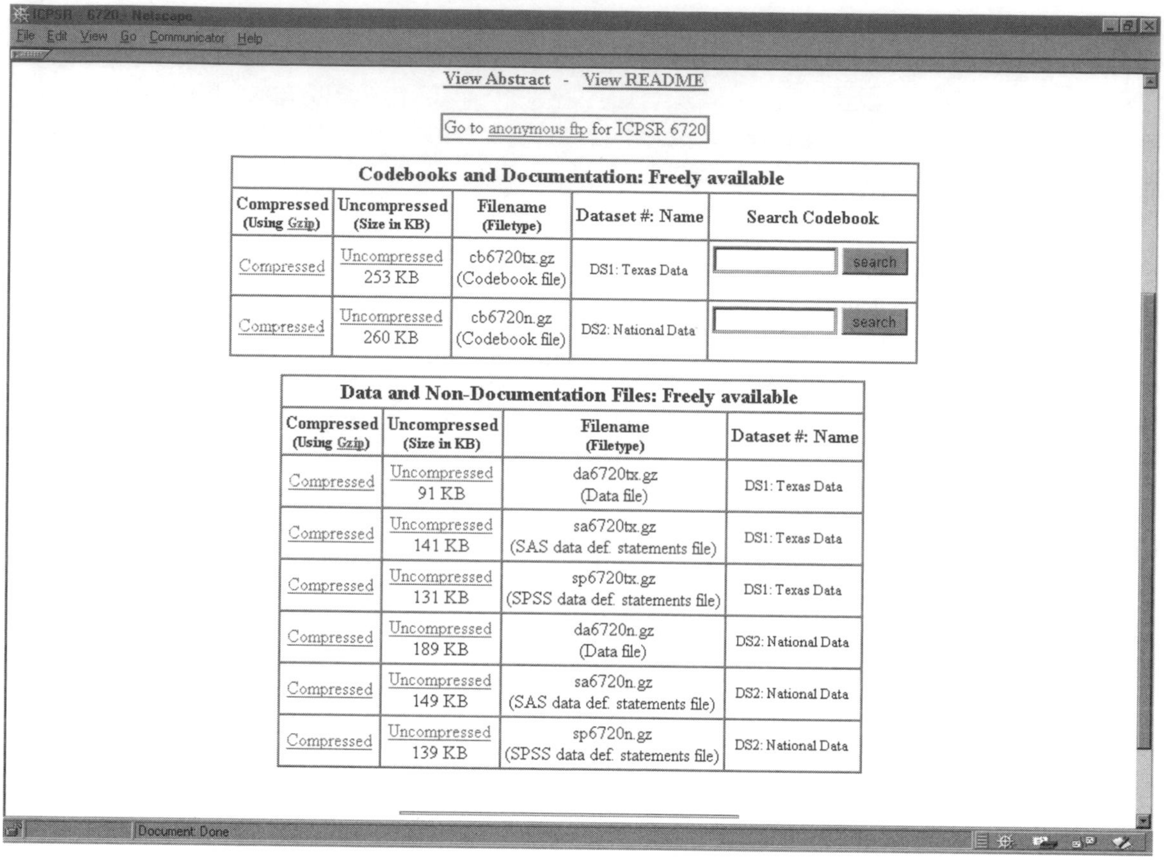

Codebooks and Documentation: Freely available				
Compressed (Using Gzip)	Uncompressed (Size in KB)	Filename (Filetype)	Dataset #: Name	Search Codebook
Compressed	Uncompressed 253 KB	cb6720tx.gz (Codebook file)	DS1: Texas Data	search
Compressed	Uncompressed 260 KB	cb6720n.gz (Codebook file)	DS2: National Data	search

Data and Non-Documentation Files: Freely available			
Compressed (Using Gzip)	Uncompressed (Size in KB)	Filename (Filetype)	Dataset #: Name
Compressed	Uncompressed 91 KB	da6720tx.gz (Data file)	DS1: Texas Data
Compressed	Uncompressed 141 KB	sa6720tx.gz (SAS data def. statements file)	DS1: Texas Data
Compressed	Uncompressed 131 KB	sp6720tx.gz (SPSS data def. statements file)	DS1: Texas Data
Compressed	Uncompressed 189 KB	da6720n.gz (Data file)	DS2: National Data
Compressed	Uncompressed 149 KB	sa6720n.gz (SAS data def. statements file)	DS2: National Data
Compressed	Uncompressed 139 KB	sp6720n.gz (SPSS data def. statements file)	DS2: National Data

Figure 13 Data screen at NACJD

Now you've seen where some of the data came from for this work-book. You could select your own study, download a codebook, and get started on using SPSS to access the data. Just keep in mind that putting a large and complex data set together may require persistence and patience. Also, many data sets are quite large so that they will not fit on a floppy disk. It may take some planning to download the codebook. Check to see whether the variables that you need are in the data set. And, from there, download SPSS data definition statements, the data, and finally save the variables you need, and lastly compress the system file. System files are smaller than raw data files. It can be a lot of work to get to this point but research is hard work and the data sets are available for you to use in your research.

Web-sites

www.icpsr.umich.edu — Inter-university Consortium for Political and Social Research

www.spss.com — Statistical Package for the Social Sciences, Inc.

Name _____   **Date** _____

*Research Problem*s;

1.   Construct a data set based on the following hypothetical data. The data represent observations
of people's driving behavior as they approached an intersection during a light change. The
questions are what factors may influence whether people follow the law and stop at a red light.
Observations are recorded during the time period the light changes from green to yellow, and
yellow to red. Observations are recorded as slowed and stopped (1), accelerated and cleared
intersection during yellow (2), accelerated and cleared intersection during red (3), ran red light
(4), blocked intersection while green and cleared intersection during red (5). Other variables
include the gender of the driver (Male as 1, and Female as 2), the driver's approximate age in
years, the type of vehicle (Car=1; Truck=2; Other=3), and whether the driver was wearing a
seatbelt recorded as yes (1), No (2), and couldn't tell (3). There are twenty cases (assign the
numbers to each category and do the data entry):

- Accelerated and red, Male, 16 years old, pick-up truck, no seat-belt
- Ran red light, Female, 25, sports car, too fast to see whether seat belt was fastened
- Blocked intersection, Male 50, sedan, seat belt
- Blocked intersection, Female, 30, minivan, seat belt
- Accelerated and yellow, Male, 25, small car, seat belt
- Accelerated and red, Male, 30, truck, no seat belt
- Accelerated and yellow, Female, 25, car, seat belt
- Blocked intersection, Male, 20, van, seat belt
- Blocked intersection, Female, 18, small car, seat belt
- Blocked intersection, Female, 75, big car, seat belt
- Blocked intersection, Male, 45, convertible, seat belt
- Accelerated and yellow, Male, 35, sedan, seat belt
- Accelerated and red, Male, 25, truck, seat belt
- Accelerated and red, Male, 30, delivery van, no seat belt visible
- Accelerated and yellow, Female, 20, small car, no seat belt visible
- Blocked intersection, Male, 30, car, seat belt
- Blocked intersection, Female, 20, car, seat belt
- Accelerated and red, Male, 20, sports car, seat belt
- Accelerated and yellow, Female, 25, sports car, seat belt
- Blocked intersection, Male, 25, truck, seat belt

Name _____   **Date** _____

Tasks
- Use the data window to create your data set.
- Ensure that all variables and values are labeled.
- Save the data set on a diskette using your name as the name of the file (e.g. Forde.sav).
- For each variable, generate the frequency distribution.

Write the frequency distribution for red-light running below.

Write a brief interpretation of these results.

Name _____   **Date** _____

2.   Design a short questionnaire that includes two questions.

Tasks
- Write out hypothetical answers to the above questions for twenty-five respondents.
- Use the data window to create your data set.
- Ensure that all variables and values are labeled.
- Save the data set on a diskette using a different name for the file (e.g. Forde Q2.sav).
- For each variable, generate a frequency distribution.

Interpretation: You will need to ensure that the completed frequency distribution provides the reader with the complete information for each variable.

Name _____   **Date** _____

The following questions will require "going an extra mile."

3.   Go to the Inter-University Consortium for Political and Social Research.

    1. Find a data set that interests you.
    2. Print the Abstract
    3. Determine the extent of documentation, and whether SPSS can be used to access the data.

4.   Go to the General Social Survey Web-site: www.icpsr.umich.edu/GSS

    1. Find two variables of interest to you.
    2. Print their codebook information.
    3. Extract these two variables including the codebooks, raw data and SPSS data definition statements. These files are generated in compressed format. Save the compressed file to a zip disk or hard drive. Use WinZip to decompress this file. Use the syntax window in SPSS to execute the commands. You must change the filename in the syntax file to note the directory on your hard drive. *This part is a difficult task for a novice but it is not impossible!*

RECODING AND COMPUTING NEW VARIABLES

INTRODUCTION

You may wish to come back to the exercises for this chapter later when you are more familiar with data analysis. It would be useful, nonetheless, to read over the examples in this chapter to learn about some of the reasons for recoding and transforming variables. Whether you're working with a data file that someone else has created or one of your own making, variables in a data file often need to be recoded in some way, or values for new variables need to be calculated based on changes in the old variables.

Some of the main reasons to recode variables are:

1. You want to change the order of the categories so that the values go from what is intuitively the lowest to highest.
2. You may have two studies that have similar variables but different coding schemes. You might recode to make them as comparable as possible.
3. You may want to recode so that you use a different statistic or procedure.
4. You may wish to recode to collapse or group a large number of categories into a few categories.
5. A recode and computation may allow you to look at combinations across several variables.

EXAMPLE 1: Reordering categories

The National Opinion Survey of Crime and Justice asked the following question:

N10 In the past year do you feel safer, not as safe or about the same on the streets in your neighborhood? **(REF 14)**

     1   Safer
     2   Not as safe
     3   About the same
M   8   Don't know
M   9   Refused

We might want to change the order on this question to reflect more "safety." How about safer (3), about the same (2) and not as safe (1)?
The frequency distribution for the original coding is shown below:

N10   HOW SAFE FEEL ON NEIGHBORHOOD STREETS

			Frequency	Percent	Valid Percent	Cumulative Percent
Valid	1	Safer	95	9.5	9.6	9.6
	2	Not as safe	186	18.5	18.9	28.5
	3	About same	704	70.0	71.5	100.0
		Total	985	98.0	100.0	
Missing	8	Dk	20	2.0		
Total			1005	100.0		

To recode, click on **TRANSFORM**, then click on **RECODE**, and then click on recode **INTO DIFFERENT VARIABLES**. It is a good idea to create a new variable rather than writing over the original (variable) because you may wish to keep the original variable for other analyses and you should verify that the changes were correct.

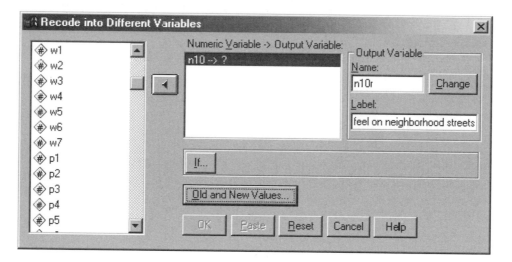

You can call the output variable anything you like (up to eight characters in length). I put an r on the end of the original name to denote "recoded." It is a good idea to put a variable label on it too. Click on "Change" to make the new variable.

Next, we are going to have to specify each of the old and new values. You must state the old and new values even if they are to stay the same. If you do not specify a particular category it will be set to system missing.

The screen below shows that 1's will be 3's, 3's will be 2's and 2's will be 1's. Enter each of the values into the old value box and the new value box, and then click "Add."

Notice that you could specify a range of old values to be recoded into a single new value. Click on "Continue" when you have all values entered.

Click on "Change" on the recode screen and "OK" to complete the recoding into a new variable.

Using the FREQUENCIES procedure, the distribution for the new variable is shown below.

N10R How safe feel on neighborhood streets

		Frequency	Percent	Valid Percent	Cumulative Percent
Valid	1.00	186	81.3	18.9	18.9
	2.00	704	7.7	71.5	90.4
	3.00	95	7.7	9.6	100.0
	Total	985	99.3	100.0	
Missing	System	20	2.0		
Total		1005	100.0		

Compare the new values to the original frequency distribution. There were 95 people who said safer (1) in the original table and there are 95 that show as 3's in this table. Check each of the other categories to see that the recode is correct. We're not done yet as it is important to label each of the categories. Go to the variable view in SPSS and add labels for each of the categories. A complete frequency distribution is shown below.

N10R   How safe feel on neighborhood streets

			Frequency	Percent	Valid Percent	Cumulative Percent
Valid	1	Not as safe	186	18.5	18.9	18.9
	2	About the same	704	70.0	71.5	90.4
	3	Safer	95	9.5	9.6	100.0
		Total	985	98.0	100.0	
Missing		System	20	2.0		
Total			1005	100.0		

What is the level of measurement of the original coding of the variable? And what is it for the new coding scheme? The answers are nominal and then ordinal. Simply changing the coding of this variable will change the types of statistics that can be used with it.

EXAMPLE 2: Collapsing some categories

The National Opinion Survey of Crime and Justice measured racial / ethnic group with the following categories:

D2   RACIAL/ETHNIC GROUP

			Frequency	Percent	Valid Percent	Cumulative Percent
Valid	1	Anglo	817	81.3	81.9	81.9
	2	Hispanic	77	7.7	7.7	89.6
	3	African	77	7.7	7.7	97.3
	4	Other	27	2.7	2.7	100.0
		Total	998	99.3	100.0	
Missing	9	Rf	7	.7		
Total			1005	100.0		

Given that there are very few people of American Indian, Asian and other origins, we might want to recode the variable so that all of these groups are combined and shown as "Other." To do this we would recode the 4, 10, and 14 categories so that they are all shown as 4's.

D2   RACIAL/ETHNIC GROUP

			Frequency	Percent	Valid Percent	Cumulative Percent
Valid	1	Anglo	817	81.3	81.9	81.9
	2	Hispanic	77	7.7	7.7	89.6
	3	African	77	7.7	7.7	97.3
	4	Other	27	2.7	2.7	100.0
		Total	998	99.3	100.0	
Missing	9	Rf	7	.7		
Total			1005	100.0		

EXAMPLE 3: Grouping categories

The General Social Survey asks people about the number of hours of television that they watch per day. It is measured as hours per day. Analyzing this kind of variable can lead to very large frequency tables. We want to collapse the categories into just a few groups and analyze this new grouping.

You should have some reason for grouping of categories. I suspect that people who watch no television are different than people who watch some t.v. and from persons who watch a lot. I will group categories as none (0 hours), some (1 or 2), and a lot (3 through the highest valid number).

The grouped frequency distribution with labels is shown below. It is very important to label variables to assist you in remembering how categories have been grouped and to assist the reader in seeing what you have done in your analysis.

TVRECODE television viewing

			Frequency	Percent	Valid Percent	Cumulative Percent
Valid	0	None	119	4.2	5.1	5.1
	1	1 or 2 hours	1141	40.3	48.8	53.9
	2	3 or more hour	1077	38.0	46.1	100.0
		Total	2337	82.5	100.0	
Missing	System		495	17.5		
Total			2832	100.0		

EXAMPLE 4 : Computing a new variable

Sometimes we would like to combine two or more variables into one new variable. We've all done this as we add up different scores on a test to get a total. There are many different arithmetic operators that can be used to combine sets of variables. We're just going to look at adding up two variables.

The General Social Survey asks people whether or not they would support abortion for any reason (ABANY) and whether they would support if a woman had been raped (ABRAPE). The coding categories on these variables are yes (1) and no (2). We would like to know how many people say yes to both questions, yes on one question, and no on all questions. What would a "yes" and "yes" add up to? The answer is 2. Combing no and no will add to 4. One no and one yes will add to 3. We can compute a new variable that will help us to analyze the combined responses.

Click on TRANSFORM and then COMPUTE. We will name a new (target) variable and then tell it how it is to be calculated. In this instance we will add abany to abrape to create a new variable which will be called abtot.

The frequency distribution for the combined variable is shown below. I have added a variable label and value labels using the variable view in the data editor.

ABTOT   Combined score of abortion for any reason and abortion for rap

			Frequency	Percent	Valid Percent	Cumulative Percent
Valid	2	Yes on both question	719	25.4	41.8	41.8
	3	Yes on one question	653	23.1	38.0	79.8
	4	No on both questions	348	12.3	20.2	100.0
		Total	1720	60.7	100.0	
Missing	System		1112	39.3		
Total			2832	100.0		

SUMMARY

In later chapters, you will see instances where it may be useful to recode or combine variables. Keep in mind that it is a good idea to create a new variable when recoding so that you can verify that the recoding was done properly. Variable and value labels are important as well. In a more advanced class, you may see that these same steps can easily be done in the syntax editor.

Importantly, if you wish to keep new variables (recoded or computed) you must save the changes to your file. If you do not, wish to, discard the file. If you make a mistake with a data file, download it again from the site or copy it from a co-student's file.

KEY TERMS

Compute
Group values
Recode

Name _____   **Date** _____

Complete the following problems.

1. Using the General Social Survey, recode AGE into four different age groups.

   a. What groupings will you use and why?

   b. Label each of the new groups

   c. Generate a frequency distribution and write it below:

2. Using the Monitoring the Future Study, recode ever used cocaine (V124) into a yes or no coding.

Name _____   **Date** _____

3. Using the Monitoring the Future Study, compute a new variable to identify whether high school students have ever drank alcohol (V103) **and** ever smoked marijuana or hashish (V115). Note that you will have to recode v115 into a yes or no format before computing the combined variable.

   a. What is the range in values for the new variable? _____ to _____

   b. Write the frequency distribution below:

4. Select a key question from one of the surveys. Use Content Select to find a research article on the same topic; or find a similar question on one of the other surveys in this workbook. Identify the similarities / differences in how the variables are measured. If different, can the variables be recoded so that results from the studies could be compared.

GRAPHING DATA

INTRODUCTION

In Chapter 1 we looked at frequency distributions. The strength of a frequency table is that it may provide detailed information about a variable whether it be counts, percentages, valid percentages or even the amount of missing data. A weakness, however, is that large tables can lead to information overload where a reader is overwhelmed by the information and he or she doesn't see the key point in a table. Graphs provide a method to visually present information from a table to highlight an important statistic or trend.

A graph is defined as a pictorial representation of a table to show variation in one variable, or differences across groups or time. Graphs aid in the interpretation of complex tables. Nonetheless, there is a trade off to be made when using a graph versus a table. We gain visual emphasis but we lose precision that was provided in the table.

This chapter introduces you to three types of graphs: pie chart, bar chart, and line graph. Additionally, this chapter will explain how to effectively display a graph and how to transform several kinds of tables into graphs.

To choose a graphical device, it is important to know the level of measurement of a variable and the number of categories or values in it. Pie and bar charts are used with nominal and ordinal level variables. As the number of categories increases, it is also more likely that a user will move from a pie chart (2-5 categories) to a bar chart. Line graphs are used with interval and ratio level variables.

PIE CHARTS

The purpose of a pie chart is to show the entire distribution of cases across categories. All categories are shown and the graph can be designed to emphasize a particular "slice" of the pie

For example, we might wonder how many Americans pray on a daily basis. The General Social Survey includes a variable on praying. The frequency distribution for praying (PRAY), in two parts, is shown on the next page.

This frequency table provides a detailed summary of the information from the 1998 General Social Survey. It is a complex table which tells us about each of the valid categories on the variable (those people that told us about how often they pray), people who didn't know or refused to answer the question. There is also a "system missing" category. This are people who were not asked this question on their version of the survey. Of the data sets for this workbook, the system missing category is particular to the General Social Survey.

```
          Statistics
```

PRAY How often does R pray

N	Valid	1428
	Missing	1404

PRAY   How often does R pray

			Frequency	Percent	Valid Percen	Cumulative Percent
Valid	1	SEVERAL TIMES A DAY	355	12.5	24.9	24.9
	2	ONCE A DAY	426	15.0	29.8	54.7
	3	SEVERAL TIMES A WEEK	202	7.1	14.1	68.8
	4	ONCE A WEEK	108	3.8	7.6	76.4
	5	LT ONCE A WEEK	313	11.1	21.9	98.3
	6	NEVER	24	.8	1.7	100.0
		Total	1428	50.4	100.0	
Missing	8	DK	3	.1		
	9	NA	14	.5		
		System	1387	49.0		
		Total	1404	49.6		
Total			2832	100.0		

   Figure 1 presents a pie chart to emphasize categories where people praying on a daily basis. That is, those Americans who pray one or more times per day.

   By taking the frequency table and presenting it as a pie chart, you should be able to quickly visualize the relative percentages of a population that fall into each category. The slices for praying once per day and several times per day are quite large. It is very easy to see that more than half of all Americans say that they pray one or more times per day.

   Next, look at the footnotes. The missing data is the total of DK and NA (3+14=17). You'll need to do this computation when you use the GSS. The total for Missing is normally provided in the Statistics table for the frequency distributions (look above).

Figure 1. How often Americans pray

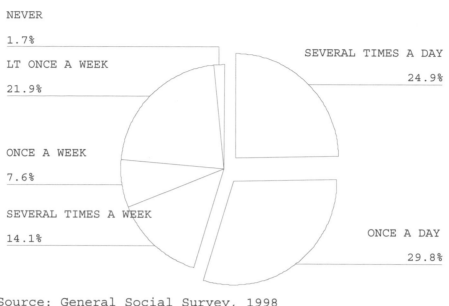

NEVER

1.7%

LT ONCE A WEEK

21.9%

ONCE A WEEK

7.6%

SEVERAL TIMES A WEEK

14.1%

SEVERAL TIMES A DAY

24.9%

ONCE A DAY

29.8%

Source: General Social Survey, 1998

N=1428   Missing = 17

A good graphical device has several features:

- Be large enough that it is easy to read
- A descriptive title
- A listing on the source of information
- The valid N and missing information should be shown
- Each slice should have a short yet descriptive label
- Percentages for each slice should be shown. Sometimes when there is a large number of categories, it is not possible to include these without "cluttering" the graph.

SPSS can be used to produce graphs. If you have access to the actual dataset you can use it to generate the information. In other cases, you may want to make a new dataset and simply enter the basic information. We will do this with a line graph.

To make the pie chart for praying, open the General Social Survey data set using SPSS. From here, look to the top line beside ANALYZE to click on "Graphs," and move down to Pie. The following dialogue box will appear.

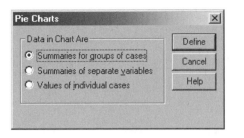

The basic pie chart provides a summary for groups of cases on a single variable. Click on define to produce the main dialogue box. We are going to select PRAY as our variable and we will tell it to define slices by % of cases.

We can enter some additional information at this point. It is important to select "options" where we will tell it to exclude missing values. By default, the program presents "percentages" and we would like it to show the "valid percentages." Try both methods and you'll see the difference.

We can type in a title and footnotes using this box. They can also be done at a later stage. Go ahead, type in this information as described earlier. Click on OK and it will generate a basic pie chart as shown on the next page.

Figure 1. How often Americans pray

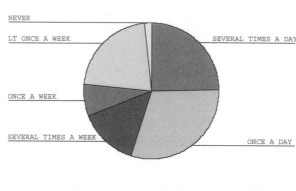

Source: General Social Survey, 1998
N=1428 Missing = 17

SPSS generates a basic pie chart using color fills, and labels that were brought in from the SPSS file. Note that the percentages for each category are missing, colors are used rather than patterns, and the footnote is centered rather than left justified. Double click on the graph and the Chart editor will open. In this editor, you may click on footnote (or click where the footnote should be) to edit it, click on each label to edit and change options, change the title, change fill patterns, and much more. You can save your chart onto a diskette and make additional changes using SPSS similar to what you would with a regular word processing file when you make revisions. You can also copy the completed chart as a picture into Microsoft word, Word Perfect, or Works. (Hint: you can impress your professor with a neat figure in a report).

BAR CHARTS

Bar charts are an effective way to show how a group (or groups) may differ on a statistic. Most often it is a valid percentage that is shown, but a bar chart can be used with means and rates. You may have seen a bar chart presenting crime rates for different cities, states, or different age groups.

Bar charts are effective because they allow a more precise presentation of information, and they can be used for a relatively large number of categories. The length of the bar is used to portray the amount of the statistic. A bar chart is used to show the specific values for each age group. It can also be used to compare percentages between groups.

An example of a bar chart is a compilation of a table on fatal traffic accidents in Memphis that I did for the Memphis Police Department. The police had a number of concerns about traffic enforcement and accidents. Source: Forde (1997).

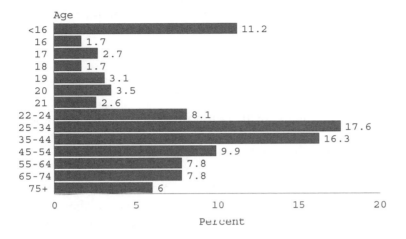

Fatal Traffic Accidents in Memphis, 1989
by Age of Victim

This horizontal bar graph shows specific information about victims between the ages of 16 and 21 and grouped information for other age groups. This was done to meet a request for detailed information on young drivers.

Bar charts are easily produced using SPSS using the GRAPH procedure. The basic bar chart is a "simple" bar chart. The initial dialogue box is shown below.

Clustered bar charts are used when you want to make comparisons on a distribution based on a second variable. For example, you might want to compare fatal traffic accident information broken down for males and females. Stacked bar charts are a more complex bar chart which is used when you want to compare distributions across groups. The stacked bar chart provides an alternative to using several charts when you wish to illustrate and compare distributions across groups.

LINE GRAPHS

Line graphs are used to examine the distribution in an interval or ratio level variable. Line graphs are very often used to demonstrate "trends" over time. They can also be used to compare two or more groups on the same graph.

For example, we might want to graph the violent crime rate in the United States. The frequency table is drawn from the Uniform Crime Reports that are published by the FBI. The violent crime rate is a rate per 100,000 persons. We will need to enter this information into SPSS. This is a very easy task to do.

Start SPSS, create two variables (Year and VCR), and then type the information into two data columns. The information from the Uniform Crime Reports follows:

Year:	Violent Crime Rate		
1980	596.6	1990	731.8
1981	594.3	1991	758.1
1982	571.1	1992	757.5
1983	537.7	1993	746.8
1984	539.2	1994	713.6
1985	556.6	1995	684.6
1986	617.7	1996	636.5
1987	609.7	1997	611.3
1988	637.2	1998	567.5
1989	663.1	1999	524.7

Once you have the data into the SPSS file, double check that you've entered the data properly. Next, go to "Graphs", select a line chart to bring up the dialogue box. In this instance, we are going to produce a simple line chart based on the values of the cases. The dialogue box follows:

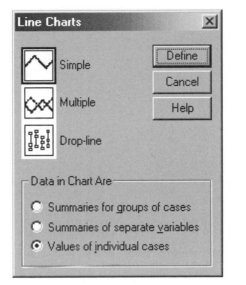

Move the variables over so that the line will represent the violent crime rate and the category labels will be the year.

You can also add a title and source at this point. The resulting line graph shows the trend in the violent crime rate in the United States over the period 1980 to 1999.

Violent Crime in the United States
1980-1999

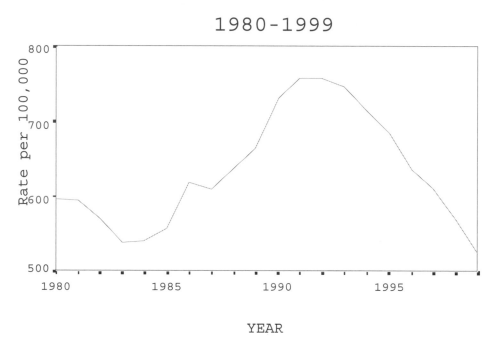

YEAR

Source: Uniform Crime Reports

A few additional changes were made to the graph using the graphics editor. First, the label VCR was changed to read as a rate per 100,000. Second, the labels for year were modified so that only every fifth year was shown and "Year" was centered.

The resulting line graph clearly shows that the violent crime rate peaked about 1992 and it has declined substantially since so that in 1999 it is at its lowest point over the entire period of 1980 to 1999.

There are additional issues that could be considered for this graph. Should the scale for the violent crime rate go from zero to 800? SPSS will choose values for a scale that go from the lowest value to the highest value. A rate of 500 for a start can potentially be misleading though. The point to be made here is that you will have to make a decision about what scale you wish to show on your graph.

FEATURES OF A GOOD GRAPH

- A title
- Nominal and ordinal level variables
  - Pie chart (if few categories)
  - Bar chart (if many)
- Interval and ratio level variables
  - Bar chart (discrete metric)
  - Line chart (discrete or continuous)
- Label slices, bars, lines, and axes
- Show percentages (if visually possible)
- Report N's
- Cite Source(s)

KEY WORDS

Bar chart
Pie chart
Line chart

Web-sites

The most recent volumes of the Federal Bureau of Investigation's Uniform Crime Reports can be read on-line:

www.fbi.gov

The *Sourcebook of Criminal Justice Statistics* has many tables that are of interest to social researchers.

www.albany.edu/sourcebook

Name _____   **Date** _____

Tasks/Interpretation: Fill in the blank for each variable.

1.   Select an appropriate graphical device for the following variables. Refer to the codebooks for information on each variable. You must determine the level of measurement for each variable. **This task can and should be completed before you go to a computer lab.**

2.   Produce a graphical device for each variable. Print the resulting graph and attach it to your homework (if requested).

3.   Write a brief interpretation of the graphical device in the space provided.

Use the Monitoring the Future Study to graph:

1.   The valid percentages for how often students report that they have used "Marijuana or hashish" in their lifetime (v115).

Name _____   **Date** _____

Use the Monitoring the Future Study to graph:

2.   Students' perception of the risk of trying crack cocaine once or twice (v1773).

Use the National Opinion Survey of Crime and Justice, 1995 to graph:

3. Americans' opinion on the most appropriate sentence for a person convicted more than once for drunk driving (C14).

Name _____   **Date** _____

Use the General Social Survey:

4.   Make a horizontal bar graph of respondent's income (Rincom98).

5.   Choose a variable from any data set.

Name _____   **Date** _____

The following data is Table 2.105 of the Sourcebook for Criminal Justice Statistics. A nationally representative sample of college freshmen were asked whether or not abortion should be legal. These data are the percentages indicating agree strongly or agree somewhat.

Year	Total Percent	Men Percent	Female Percent
1977	55.7	55.8	55.6
1978	56.7	56.5	56.9
1979	53.3	53.0	53.6
1980	53.6	53.3	53.8
1981	53.9	53.0	54.7
1982	54.8	53.7	55.9
1983	54.8	54.7	54.8
1984	53.8	53.3	54.2
1985	54.9	54.5	55.3
1986	58.6	58.3	59.0
1987	58.7	58.7	58.7
1988	57.0	56.8	57.2
1989	64.7	63.6	65.5
1990	64.9	65.0	64.8
1991	63.0	63.0	63.0
1992	64.1	63.9	64.2
1993	62.4	61.8	62.8
1994	59.7	59.0	60.3
1995	58.4	57.8	58.9
1996	56.3	55.7	56.7
1997	53.5	53.7	53.3
1998	50.9	52.5	49.5
1999	52.7	53.8	51.7
2000	53.9	54.5	53.5

Maguire, K. & Pastore, A.L. (Eds.) (2001) *Sourcebook of Criminal Justice Statistics* [Online]. Available: http://www.albany.edu/sourcebook/ [May 3, 2002].

6. Produce a line graph for one of these trends. Label it and interpret the trend. If you care to go the extra mile, locate the Sourcebook online to get additional information about the original sources used to compile this table.

Name _____   **Date** _____

7.   Using the General Social Survey, what kind of graphical device would you recommend for hours per day watching television (TVHOURS)? Explain your choice.

8.   Recode TVHOURS and produce a pie-chart.

MEASURES OF CENTRAL TENDENCY

INTRODUCTION

There are three commonly used measures of central tendency: mode, median, and mean. The mode is simply the most common score, the median is the middle case in a distribution, and the mean is the arithmetic average.

The shape of a distribution, however, can influence whether the mean is an appropriate statistic. Unusual scores will distort a distribution from "normal" and when this happens we select the median as a better measure than the mean.

If a distribution is symmetric, the mean and median will be the same value. If a distribution is positively skewed, the mean will be pulled to the right. If it is negatively skewed, the mean will be pulled to the left. If a distribution is skewed, the median will fall between the mode and the mean and the median will be a better measure of the average. We can look at a bar chart and make our best guess about whether to use the mean or the median.

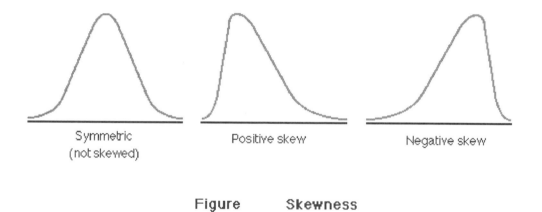

Symmetric   Positive skew   Negative skew
(not skewed)

Figure   Skewness

For example, suppose that we have a summer class with 20 students in it. The combined income of 19 of them is $80,000 and we have "Super Dunk" (a Basketball Player making about 5 million dollars a year). The mean income for the entire class is $254,000. Is it reasonable to say the average income of students is $254,000? No! The distribution is skewed to the right by an outlying case so that the median value of $4500 is a better measure of the average.

In social science research we also have to assess the shape of distributions. Marvin Wolfgang and his colleagues long ago showed us that a small number of juveniles commit the vast majority of delinquent acts. How about the average for police use of excessive force? Fortunately, it is relatively unusual. Or, fear of crime? Extremely high levels of fear occur but they also are unusual.

The objectives of this chapter are to introduce measures of central tendency and to demonstrate how the shape of the distribution of a variable may influence measures of central tendency. In particular, you will look to see how the mean of a distribution may be biased by the skew of a distribution. You will:

1.   look at the shape of a distribution using a histogram;
2.   guess whether the median or the mean is larger; and
3.   compare your estimate from the histogram to the actual values.

DATA ANALYSIS

In Chapter 1 you generated a table of the frequency distribution for a number of variables. Graphic presentations can also be effectively used to illustrate the shape of a distribution. A reader can see where scores fall and can estimate what the average score is in a distribution. Bar graphs and line graphs are commonly used to examine interval (or ordinal variables when we make an assumption that can be treated as interval level) and ratio level variables. These variables are treated as if they were continuous to emphasize continuity along the length of a scale. Usually, the values of a variable are grouped into class intervals of equal size. For example, hours of t.v. watching could alternatively be grouped into half- hour intervals; or age could be grouped in five, ten, or one year intervals.

The histograms in SPSS look very much like the bar charts you saw in the last chapter. They are generated as a "chart" in the FREQUENCIES procedure. In a histogram, the relative length of the bar equals the relative frequency for the class interval. By looking at the shape of the histogram we can get an idea of skewedness (symmetry) and peakedness (or kurtosis) of a distribution. We would like to know whether the distribution is symmetric or skewed, and whether the kurtosis is flat, peaked, or normal. Today we will just consider whether a variable is skewed or normal. Again, the reason to conduct this analysis is that we want to know whether the mean is an appropriate statistic for a distribution.

The distribution of a variable is symmetrical when scores look the same on both sides of the middle. A distribution is asymmetrical when scores fall to one side or the other. When there is a substantial difference in movement of scores we call this a skewed distribution. A distribution is a positive (or right-tail) skew when extreme scores fall to the right of center. A distribution is negative (or left-tail) when extreme scores fall to the left of center. For example, how often a person worries about getting murdered is left-skewed as few people very frequently worry about getting murdered. In fact most Americans don't ever worry about it (modal category). Respondents are grouped on the right indicating that they never worry about getting murdered. Is this an interesting result from the study? Does it fit with what you may have heard on TV or from a newspaper?

You will study three measures of central tendency: mode, median, and mean. Your text shows that the level of measurement is one criterion for selecting a measure of central tendency. This Chapter demonstrates a second criterion – skew – which, when present, biases the mean so that it is no longer useful as a measure of central tendency.

The mean is sensitive to extreme scores. The mean will be pulled to the side where the extreme scores are located. In a left-tail skew the value of the mean will be less than the median. In a right-tail distribution the mean will be greater than the median. In a symmetric or normal distribution they have the same value.

DATA ANALYSIS EXAMPLE USING FOX'S CALCULATOR

Research problem:

Truancy is a problem in many urban school systems. A researcher gathers data for a random sample of twenty students in a middle school. The raw data on unexcused absences where a child missed school without a legitimate reason (e.g. sickness) are as follows:

$$0, 0, 1, 1, 0, 0, 1, 2, 0, 19, 0, 0, 1, 1, 10, 2, 0, 0, 1, 2$$

Enter these twenty cases into the FREQUENCY DISTRIBUTIONS option in Fox's Statistics calculator. The results are shown below.

File Edit View Insert Format Tools Chart Window Help

FREQUENCY DISTRIBUTIONS

For grouped frequency distribution fill in below

Starting value	0	20 Categoriezed
Ending value	20	0 Not categorized
#Class Intervals	10	◄ ► Select
Size (calculated)	2.00	with buttons

Fill in data values below

X: 0, 0, 0, 0, 0, 0, 0, 0, 0, 1, 1, 1, 1, 1, 1, 2, 2, 2, 10, 19

N	20	Range	19
Min	0	Mean Dev	2.490
Max	19	Var (s^2)	19.748
Mode	0	SD (s)	4.444
Median	1	estVar (s^2)	20.787
Mean ($\bar{X}$)	2.050	estSD (s)	4.559

Class intervals	m	f	%	cf	c%
From 0.0 up to 2.0	1.00	15	75.0%	15	75.0%
From 2.0 up to 4.0	3.00	3	15.0%	18	90.0%
From 4.0 up to 6.0	5.00	0	0.0%	18	90.0%
From 6.0 up to 8.0	7.00	0	0.0%	18	90.0%
From 8.0 up to 10.0	9.00	0	0.0%	18	90.0%
From 10.0 up to 12.0	11.00	1	5.0%	19	95.0%
From 12.0 up to 14.0	13.00	0	0.0%	19	95.0%
From 14.0 up to 16.0	15.00	0	0.0%	19	95.0%
From 16.0 up to 18.0	17.00	0	0.0%	19	95.0%
From 18.0 thru 20.0	19.00	1	5.0%	20	100.0%
Total		20	100.0%		

Percentage Distribution

(bar chart: Percent axis 0% to 80%, Midpoint axis with values 1.00, 5.00, 9.00, 13.00, 17.00)

The data is entered into the box on the left. I sorted the values from highest to lowest prior to typing in the values. You can do this or just enter them from the list. In order to get a histogram, you have to enter a starting and ending value, and the number of class intervals. I chose the "minimum" as the starting value and 20 as my maximum values. I chose 10 as the number of class intervals. This is the number of bars that will be shown in the percentage distribution.

Look back at the figure on skewness (on page XX) and compare it to the percentage distribution above. What does it look like? My guess is that it is skewed to the right so that we will expect a mean that is larger than the median. Is this correct? The statistics are calculated as a mean of 2.05 and a median of 1. The mean is larger than the median. Where is the mode? It is at 0. The median falls between the mean and the mode. It does appear that we have a positively skewed distribution. Most students have zero unexcused absences (mode=0). The average number of unexcused absences is one class (Median = 1). The mean is probably not a good measure of central tendency in this case because of extreme scores. One student had 19 unexcused absences.

Fox's calculator is very useful when you have a small number of cases to analyze. SPSS is a more powerful tool when you wish to work with large data files. It also calculates a statistic that estimates the degree of skewness.

DATA ANALYSIS EXAMPLE USING SPSS

Research Problem: Is the distribution of ratings of the situation where respondents worry about getting murdered symmetric or skewed? (W5)   Is the mean or the median a better estimate of the central tendency of the distribution? We will obtain a skewness statistic to assess whether or not the distribution can be considered as "normal." If the skewness is **greater that 2.0 in magnitude**, we will say that the distribution is skewed and that the mean is no longer an appropriate measure of central tendency. If this happens, we rely upon the median as our best estimate of the average.   If the skewness is **less than 2.0 in magnitude**, we will say that the distribution is symmetric and that the mean is the most appropriate measure of central tendency.

Histograms in SPSS: Histograms provide a pictorial representation of frequency distributions. The computer program will modify the class intervals so that they fit on a single page. The length of the bar represents the frequency of occurrence for a class interval. The length of bars are approximate. The class intervals are bounded by the smallest valid number (left-end) and the largest valid number. The middle value of an interval is the mid-point of a class interval. For each histogram, note the definition of the interval width. It doesn't have to be one unit.

Computer output: The following histogram shows the distribution for "worry about getting murdered." Find W5 in the National Opinion Survey of Crime and Justice codebook.

The histogram shows several things. First, the mode is located by finding the longest bar in the histogram. It is a score of "4." Reading the codebook, we see that the modal category (mode) is such that most Americans never worry about getting murdered. The count in the histogram is equivalent to the valid frequency that is reported in a frequency distribution. We see that somewhere close to 600 of 1003 people said that they never worry about getting murdered.

Next, we will make a guess as to whether the distribution is skewed and if so we will guess whether the mean or the median will be larger. We suspect that there is a negative skew; few Americans say seldom (3) and very few say somewhat frequently (2) or very frequently (1). Therefore, we guess that the mean will be smaller than the median. Keep in mind that this is just a guess. We will calculate a skewness statistic to see whether our guess was accurate in order to make a decision about whether the mean or the median is a better measure of the average for the variable.

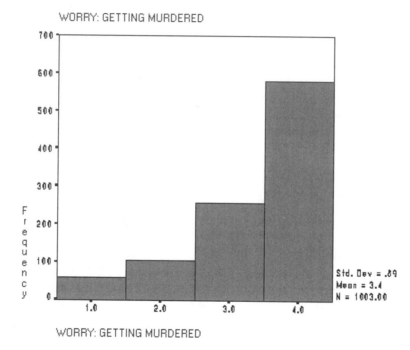

WORRY: GETTING MURDERED

Computer work: We will use a statistical test to assess our guess about skewness and the placement of the mean and median. The criterion for a significant difference is that skewness is greater than 2.0 to indicate a significant difference between the mean and median. We use the FREQUENCIES procedure, as in Chapter 1, select statistics, and then check the appropriate boxes to obtain statistics. Below you can see that the mean, median, and skewness are checked. Click on "Continue" to move back to the main dialogue box in FREQUENCIES and then click OK.

The results of the statistical analysis are shown in the table. The Skewness is –1.264. Our criterion was that it had to be above 2 in magnitude in order for us to say that the distribution was skewed. Thus, we see that the mean is smaller than the median but it is not substantially different than the median. We conclude that the mean is an appropriate measure of central tendency and we would provide an interpretation of it in our overall summary.

```
                              Statistics
```

W5 WORRY: GETTING MURDERED		
N	Valid	1003
	Missing	2
Mean		3.36
Median		4.00
Skewness		-1.264
Std. Error of Skewness		.077

Interpretation: An analysis of the distribution in public opinion about American's worry over getting murdered was conducted. This variable was operationalized using a scale where "1" means that a persons worries very frequently and "4" means that they never worry. For this variable, the best indicator of the average is the mean because the distribution is approximately normal (sk=-1.3). In a normal distribution the mean is a better measure of the average score than the median. The mean score for this question was 3.3 on a scale of 1 to 4. A mean of 3.3 indicates that an average American seldom worries about getting murdered.

Note that an interpretation should describe:

- The source of information
- The scale (in this case a question on a survey)
- The analysis (in this case an assessment of skewness)
- The decision (that the mean is the best measure of central tendency for this variable)
- And an interpretation of what the mean means.

KEY TERMS

Bias   Skewness
Central Tendency
Histogram
Mean
Median
Mode

Research Problems:

Calculate the mode, median and mean for each variable. Use the percentage distribution or histograms for each variable to estimate whether there is a significant skew in the distributions.

Tasks:

1.   For each of the variables, identify the level of measurement.
2.   Use the histograms to find the mode. Make your guess about skewness and estimate where the mean will fall in relation to the median.
3.   Use the computer to find the mean, median, and skewness.
4.   For each variable, write a short summary of two or three sentences. You should describe the skew of the distribution and indicate which measure of central tendency is best for the distribution.

Name _____   **Date** _____

1.   Use Fox's Statistics Calculator to analyze the following data.

A researcher examines court dispositions on sentencing where different judges make sentencing recommendations for very similar convictions. Twenty cases were identified and sentence length in years is shown below:

1, 3, 2, 6, 6, 15, 3, 3, 2, 1, 25, 3, 3, 2, 1, 2, 2, 4, 5, 2

For the percentage distribution, use a starting value of 0, an ending value of 25 and number of intervals of 5.

What is the level of measurement?

Draw the percentage distribution below (roughly)

From the percentage distribution, where do you think the mean falls?

Is the mean or median bigger? (circle guess)

Name _____   **Date** _____

From the Statistics Calculator:

Mean _____

Median _____

Mode _____

Which measure is best: Mean / Median (Circle)

Interpretation of results:

Going beyond the output: Use Content Select to find an article on "sentencing disparity." Write a short essay on why this issue is important to study.

Name _____   **Date** _____

2.   From the National Opinion Survey of Crime and Justice, hours of t.v. watched per week (M4)

Use the codebook to complete the following:

Variable name

Level of Measurement

Guess: Mean or median is bigger (circle guess)

HOW MANY HOURS WATCH TV PER WEEK

Std. Dev = 11.46
Mean = 15.0
N = 966.00

HOW MANY HOURS WATCH TV PER WEEK

What is the mode?   _____

71

Name _____   **Date** _____

Use the computer to calculate:

Mean _____

Median _____

Skewness _____

Which measure is best: Mean / Median (Circle)

Interpretation of results:

Going beyond the output: Use Content Select to find an article on television viewing habits. Write a short essay on your findings.

Name _____   **Date** _____

3.   From the NOSCJ, analyze the distribution in public opinion about the neighborhood problem of people being drunk or high in public (N7).

Use the codebook to complete the following:

Variable name

Level of Measurement

Guess: Mean or median is bigger (circle)

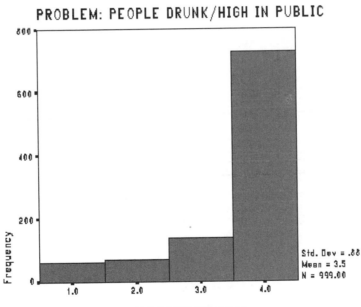

PROBLEM: PEOPLE DRUNK/HIGH IN PUBLIC

Std. Dev = .88
Mean = 3.5
N = 999.00

PROBLEM: PEOPLE DRUNK/HIGH IN PUBLIC

What is the mode?

Name _____   **Date** _____

Use the computer to calculate:

Mean _____

Median _____

Skewness _____

Which measure is best: Mean / Median (Circle)

Interpretation of results:

Going beyond the output: Use Content Select to find an article on "neighborhood disorder." Why is this an important issue for people's quality of life?

Name _____   **Date** _____

4.   From the General Social Survey, analyze the distribution of family income (Income98).

Use the codebook to complete the following:

Variable name

Level of Measurement

Guess: Mean or median is bigger (circle)

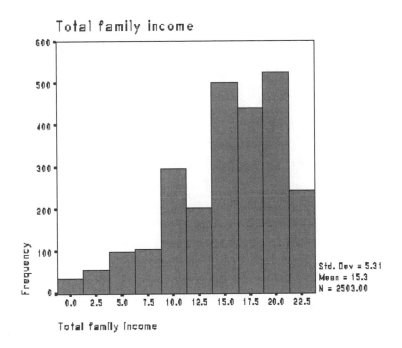

Total family income

What is the mode?

Name _____   **Date** _____

Use the computer to calculate:

Mean _____

Median _____

Skewness _____

Which measure is best: Mean / Median (Circle)

Interpretation of results:

Going beyond the output: Use Content Select to find an article on "income inequality."
Write a short essay on the distribution of family income in America.

Name _____   **Date** _____

5.   From the GSS, political views (Polviews).

Use the codebook to complete the following:

Variable name

Level of Measurement

Guess: Mean or median is bigger (circle)

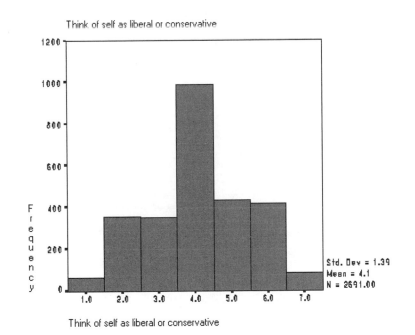

Think of self as liberal or conservative

Std. Dev = 1.39
Mean = 4.1
N = 2691.00

Think of self as liberal or conservative

What is the mode?

Name _____   **Date** _____

Computer calculations of:

Mean _____

Median _____

Skewness _____

Which measure is best: Mean / Median (Circle)

Interpretation of results:

Going beyond the output: Use Content Select to find an article on "political values." Compare these results from the 1998 GSS with the article.

Z-SCORES AND THE NORMAL CURVE

INTRODUCTION

This chapter introduces properties of the normal curve and uses the standard deviation to critically assess whether a distribution is a "normal" distribution. If it is not, there are substantial implications about whether the mean and standard deviation are appropriate statistics. You will:

1. look at measures of variability;
2. use the mean and standard deviation to compute z-scores; and
3. compare the observed (empirical) distribution of variables to a normal distribution.

Measures of Variability

Measures of variability describe the amount of dispersion in a variable. Selecting a measure depends on the level of analysis of a variable. The range (R) is a simple measure of variability, applicable for ordinal variables and higher, where you take the difference between the smallest (minimum) and largest (maximum) score. The variance (s^2) and standard deviation (s), applicable to interval and ratio level variables, are the most commonly used measures of variation. The variance is a measure that looks at how far each score is above or below the mean score in a distribution, and it takes into account how many cases are in the population. We will generate these statistics from the sample and make inferences about the population parameters.

The mean and the standard deviation are two of the basic building blocks which form the foundation of most elementary and advanced statistics. A key assumption for many of the statistics that we will use in later chapters in this workbook is that a variable is normally distributed. This chapter provides a method to test this assumption whereby we can describe with great precision the dispersion in a variable.

Ultimately, while we are working with sample statistics for the mean (x) and standard deviation (s) we are doing this to estimate the true population parameters of the mean (μ) and standard deviation (σ) of a population. Consider the Monitoring the Future Study which examines a sample of high school seniors yet we wish to generalize to all high school seniors in the United States.

Z-scores

In order to conduct our test, we will need to convert the scores on a variable into a standard score or z-score. A z-score is a standardized score showing the difference between a particular score (x) and the population mean (μ) taking into account the standard deviation of the variable (σ).

The z-score shows, in standard units, where a case falls in a normal distribution.

$$z = (x-\mu) / \sigma$$

You may convert raw scores to standard scores; or you may convert z-scores into raw scores.
$$x = \mu + z\,(\sigma).$$

Normal distribution

The standard normal distribution (bell curve) is symmetric with a mean of zero and a standard deviation of 1. We know the theoretical area under the curve for any specified z-score. Using Appendix C in Levin and Fox, the z-score table shows that there is 34.13% of the area under the curve as we go from the mean (0) to one standard deviation above the mean (1). Figure 1 below shows a graphical presentation of this area. How much area is there between 0 and −1? It's the same distance as from 0 to +1. Thus, the answer is also 34.13. Find the area in the Appendix going from 0 to +2 standard deviations. And, from 0 to +3 standard deviations. The answers are 47.72% and 49.84%.

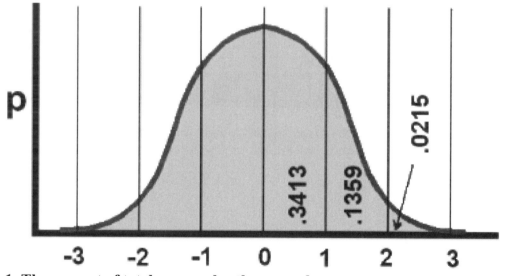

Figure 1. The percent of total area under the normal curve

To complete a "strong test" of the fit of a variable empirical distribution with the normal curve we would like to examine every 1 unit area under the curve: 0-1; 1-2; and 2-3 on both sides of the curve. From the normal curve, we know the theoretical distribution of cases. We will use the actual mean and standard deviation to calculate the expected distribution for a variable and compare the observed values to expected values.

The vast majority of z-scores usually fall within three standard deviations of the mean. Thus, we will limit our test for all practical purposes to scores that fall within −3 to + 3 standard deviations from the mean.

The area under the bell curve is used to make statements about probability of occurrence of the distribution of cases. Researchers typically are interested in how many cases fall within 1, 2, and 3 standard deviations of the mean as 34.1%; 13.6%, and 2.1%. To complete our test, we will use a criterion of + or − 5% on the difference between the observed and theoretical percentages in each interval.   If we find that all intervals fit this criterion, we will say that we have a strong fit to the normal distribution.   If any of the intervals fail to meet this criterion, we do not have a strong fit.

In many instances a variable may be close to normal where most cases are near the center of the distribution but with a slight skew to one side. We can relax our assessment by adjusting our test to see whether cases fall within –1 to +1 standard deviations; -2 to 2; and –3 to 3. Figure 2 shows the approximate areas under the curve in these intervals. If our test using a criterion of + or – 5% shows a fit to the distribution, we will call this a weak fit to the normal distribution. In fact, in many instances this is what we are going to find.

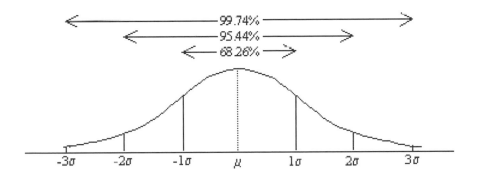

Figure 2. The percent of total area for the weak fit to the normal curve

The z-scores in a normal distribution are "theoretical." The degree to which these characteristics are found for a variable depends on the "observed" distribution of the variable. A variable which is skewed may only approximate a few of the characteristics of a normal distribution. A variable which is highly skewed may not have any of these characteristics.

When we complete the exercises for this chapter we will use a table as shown below to make our assessment of fit.

z-score	-3 to -2	-2 to –1	-1 to 0	0 to 1	1 to 2	2 to 3
Strong fit	2.1%	13.6%	34.1%	34.1%	13.6%	2.1%
Weak fit for total areas			68%			
		95%				
	99.74%					

For example, we expect about 34.1 % of cases to fall within 1 standard deviation above the mean. The table below shows the approximate number of cases under the curve for each interval.

DATA ANALYSIS EXAMPLE

Research problem: What is the distribution of high school students' average letter grade? Think about it for a moment. What would a distribution look like if most students get A's and B's and few students get C's and D's. Draw out a rough picture for yourself. Or, how about a situation where most students get C's and D's and very few get A's and B's? We will use the Monitoring the Future Study to compare the actual distribution of average grades to the normal curve. We will assess whether there is a strong or a weak fit of the observed distribution compared to theoretical expectations for a normal curve.

Codebook information: Use the codebook to get the basic information on level of measurement.

Codebook information		Statistics	
Variable name	V179	Mean	
Variable label	Average grade so far in High School	SD	
Minimum	1 "D"	Variance	
Maximum	9 "A"	Range	
Metric	1 partial letter grade (+/- system)	Valid cases	
Level of Measurement	Interval / scale		

Use the computer to obtain *descriptive statistics*:   In order to calculate the z-scores we are going to need a mean and standard deviation. We can obtain the range and variance at the same time. Click on Analyze, Descriptive Statistics, and then descriptives. Click in the box

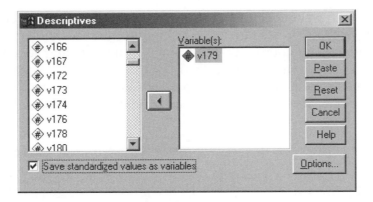

to save standardized values as variables. This will create a new variable ZG3 which is G3 turned into z-scores.   You'll also need to click on options to select the Range and variance.

As you complete the exercise, write the mean, standard deviation, range and variance into the earlier table. The SPSS output from the DESCRIPTIVES procedure is show below:

Descriptive Statistics

V179 002C20 :R HS GRADE/D=1	4313	1	9	6.08	1.968
Valid N (listwise)	4313				

We're going to use the mean and standard deviation to calculate the continuous and discrete raw scores that would be expected if the observed variable is truly a normal distribution. This is the formula: $x = \mu + z(\sigma)$ where we will insert the mean and standard deviation to calculate the lower interval for the continuous raw score.

For example, at –4 standard deviations x= 6.08 + -4(1.97) ; x= -1.80. Write this number into the column for the lower bound of the continuous raw score for –4. Find –1.80 in the Table on the next page. Calculate the lower limit for –3.   That is x= 6.08 + -3(1.97) = +0.17. Repeat these calculations for all of the lower limits. The solutions are shown in the Table.

What is the expected value at 0 standard deviations from the mean? The answer is the mean. Since we know this, use this a back-up check on your calculations.

Next, we will estimate the upper limit as the next number between the upper limit and the lower limit for the adjacent interval. For example, if the lower limit for –3 to –2 is 0.17 then the next smallest number is 0.16. Do this for all of the intervals except the last one. You can estimate it if you calculate another z-score for +5 on the lower limit or you can just say it is expected to be any z-score higher than 11.99.

83

Next, we're going to want to determine the theoretical values for discrete scores in each interval. This is easy! Just look to see the smallest whole number in an interval and the largest whole number in an interval. Of course, we only want to work with numbers that were on our original survey question. Recall that it went from 1 (D) to 9 (A). Thus, we need to find out where scores of 1 to 9 fall in the theoretical normal distribution. When expected values come up as a number that falls outside the possible numbers on our scale then we will note these as not applicable (NA).

| Class intervals | | | | | | Distribution | |
| Continuous z-score | | Continuous raw Score | | Discrete raw Score | | % of cases per interval | |
Lower	Upper	Lower	Upper	Lower	Upper	Observed	Expected
-4	-3	--1.80	0.16				
-3	-2	0.17	2.13				
-2	-1	2.14	4.10				
-1	0	4.11	6.07				
0	1	6.08	8.04				
1	2	8.05	10.01				
2	3	10.02	11.98				
3	4	11.99	Higher				

Where does "1" go? Can it go between −1.80 and 0.16? No. A zero could fit in here as an integer but it is not a part of our scale. Most to the next interval between 0.17 and 2.13. Does it fit here? Yes, 1 is the lowest whole number (discrete raw score) between 0.17 and 2.13. What is the largest whole number that fits in this interval? Can "2" go in? Yes. How about 3? No. 3 is larger than 2.13. Our upper bound for this interval is 2.

For the next interval, 2.14 to 4.10, what values fit here? How about 2? No, it is too small. The answers are 3 is the lower limit and 4 is the upper limit. The completed table is shown on the following page. Not applicable (n.a.) is noted in intervals where no values are possible. These discrete values represent the scores for letter grades if the actual distribution conforms with what is expected in a normal distribution.

We're ready to complete the table by obtaining a frequency distribution for the variable. We know the expected distribution as the area that falls under the normal curve.

We will complete the table by generating a frequency distribution to find the observed frequencies. Wow. Are you overwhelmed yet? We're almost there.

```
              V179   002C20 :R HS GRADE/D=1
```

			Frequency	Percent	Valid Percent	Cumulative Percent
Valid	1	D:(1)	57	1.2	1.3	1.3
	2	C-:(2)	141	2.9	3.3	4.6
	3	C:(3)	286	5.9	6.6	11.2
	4	C+:(4)	464	9.5	10.8	22.0
	5	B-:(5)	604	12.4	14.0	36.0
	6	B:(6)	852	17.5	19.8	55.7
	7	B+:(7)	765	15.7	17.7	73.5
	8	A-:(8)	611	12.5	14.2	87.6
	9	A:(9)	533	10.9	12.4	100.0
		Total	4313	88.4	100.0	
Missing	-9	Missing	564	11.6		
Total			4877	100.0		

Class intervals						Distribution	
Continuous z-score		Continuous raw score		Discrete raw score		% of cases per interval	
Lower	Upper	Lower	Upper	Lower	Upper	Observed	Expected
-4	-3	-1.80	0.16	n.a.	n.a.	0.0	0
-3	-2	0.17	2.13	1	2	4.6	2.1
-2	-1	2.14	4.10	3	4	17.4	13.6
-1	0	4.11	6.07	5	6	33.8	34.1
0	1	6.08	8.04	7	8	31.9	34.1
1	2	8.05	10.01	9	9	12.4	13.6
2	3	10.02	11.98	n.a.	n.a.	0	2.1
3	4	11.99	higher	n.a.	n.a.	0	0

How many not applicable raw scores do you see if the frequency distribution? That is, scores that fall outside 1 to 9? The answer is 0. Write 0.0 in for each of the n.a.'s. What percentage of grades fall between 1 and 2? To get this, add up the percentages for 1 and 2 to get 4.6 percent. Write this percentage into the interval. What percentage of scores are 3 and 4? Add 6.6 and 10.8 percent to get 17.4. Continue adding up the percentages for each intervals. The remaining information is shown in the chart and we finally are ready to assess the fit of the observed distribution to the normal curve.

Assessing fit: We will always use a criterion of five percent to decide whether or not there is a difference in the percentage of cases in the observed versus the normal distribution. Simply subtract the observed percentage from the expected percentage for each interval to see whether the difference is more than 5 percent (lower or higher). In this example, the distribution clearly fits the strong version of the empirical distribution. There are no instances larger than than would be expected (e.g. 4.6 - 2.1 = 2.5; 17.4 - 13.6 =3.8; etc.). This clearly shows that the distribution fits the strong test of whether it is a normal distribution.

A distribution that fits the strong version will always fit the weak version of the empirical distribution. If the strong version fails, we should see if there is a weak fit to the normal curve? We will test the weak fit below to illustrate the calculations to add up the cases between each of the intervals.

In this example, which cases fall between −1 as a lower limit and +1 as an upper limit? That is, which raw scores are expected to fall between −1 and + 1 standard deviations? The answer is discrete scores of 5 through 8. What percentage of observed cases fell in this interval? Add up the following: 14.0+19.8+17.7+14.2 = 65.7.

Comparison for weak distribution	% Observed	% Expected
+/- 1 SD	65.7	68
+/- 2 SD	95.5	95
+/- 3 SD	100.0	99.75%

Do the same calculations for scores between −2 and +2 and −3 and +3 standard deviations. The solutions are shown in the Table above. We again use a criterion of +/- 5 percent to assess the fit of the weak version of the empirical distribution subtracting the observed from the expected percentage of cases. In all instances the differences are less than 5 percent. We would say that the distribution fits the weak version of the empirical distribution.

If there was a difference of +/- 5 percent in any of the intervals we would say that the test of fit had failed. In this example, we found a perfect fit for the strong version of the empirical distribution and a perfect fit for the weak version of the empirical distribution. The importance of this finding is that the distribution of the variable is normally distributed so that its mean and standard deviation are appropriate statistics. We've done a very rigorous test to determine whether we should be using a mean and standard deviation with this variable.

In your statistics course you will see that the mean and standard deviation are the foundation for most sophisticated statistical tests. When a variable fails to fit the strong version of the empirical distribution then it may not be appropriate to use sophisticated statistical tests. When a variable has a weak fit we will usually continue to use these more advanced statistics but provide a qualifier about our results. If a statistical test assumes a normal distribution, you can test this using the methods outlined in this chapter.

It is important in any data analysis that you go beyond the computer output. You should summarize the information so that a reader can understand the basic information you wish to present. Telling someone about a z-score of 1.0 is not all that meaningful. You should refer back to an original metric (if there is one).

Interpretation: We conducted a test to assess the distribution of American high school students' average letter grades using data from the Monitoring the Future study. We compared the actual percentages of cases to a normal distribution and found that students' letter grades fit the strong weak version of the empirical distribution. This test assesses whether a variable is normally distributed. We conclude that it is appropriate to use a mean or a standard deviation in future analysis of this variable. The mean letter is approximately a B (M=6.1) with a standard deviation of 2.0. We conclude that this variable is normally distributed.

We're done! We've done an incredible amount of work in order to assess whether the mean and standard deviation are appropriate statistics. If there is a strong fit, they clearly apply. If there is a weak fit, they probably can still be used but the researcher should explain to the reader that there may be problems. If the distribution does not fit, then the mean and standard deviation should not be used and the analyst should recommend that the median and range be used. This is a time consuming test, but it is important that a researcher know the properties of data that he or she is using in more complex tests.

Note that we can obtain the same information by examining the frequency distribution of the transformed variable. It's frequency distribution is shown below. The raw "1" translates into a z-score of –2.58210. We could use this table looking for values between – 4 and –3 with none; -3 to –2 and 4.7 percent; and continuing on down.

ZV179   Zscore: 002C20 :R HS GRADE/D=1

		Frequency	Percent	Valid Percent	Cumulative Percent
Valid	-2.58210	57	1.2	1.3	1.3
	-2.07386	141	2.9	3.3	4.6
	-1.56562	286	5.9	6.6	11.2
	-1.05738	464	9.5	10.8	22.0
	-.54913	604	12.4	14.0	36.0
	-.04089	852	17.5	19.8	55.7
	.46735	765	15.7	17.7	73.5
	.97559	611	12.5	14.2	87.6
	1.48384	533	10.9	12.4	100.0
	Total	4313	88.4	100.0	
Missing	System	564	11.6		
Total		4877	100.0		

Either method will allow a test of the fit of the distribution to the normal curve. Calculation of the continuous and discrete raw scores though should give you a greater appreciation on how to convert standard to raw scores and vice versa.

KEY TERMS

Descriptives
Normal curve
Standard deviation
Strong fit
Weak fit
Z-score

CHAPTER 6 PROBLEMS

Research Problems: Summarize the statistical variation of the following variables from the General Social Survey, 1998:

1. Respondent's income. (Rincom98) M=13.28, SD= 5.25
2. How often people read the newspaper (News) M= 2.18, SD= 1.31
3. Frequency of having sex during last year (Sexfreq)
4. How often respondent prays (Pray)

Tasks:
1. Use the codebook to identify the characteristics of variables (assume that ordinal variables are at the interval level). Copy the information for each variable on to worksheets; each worksheet is for one variable.
2. The means and standard deviations for Rincom98 and news are provided above. Use this information to calculate the continuous and discrete raw scores prior to coming into the computer lab.
3. Use the descriptives procedure in SPSS for windows to get the remaining statistics for rincom98 and news and all of the statistics for sexfreq and pray (mean, standard deviation, variance, range, and valid cases). Write the statistics on to the worksheets.
4. Use SPSS for windows to obtain a frequency distribution for each variable. Copy the information from each z-score distribution to the worksheets.
5. Calculate the continuous and discrete class intervals for each variable. Compare the observed (empirical) distributions with the normal distribution.

Interpretations: For each variable, write a short summary of the variable using the mean, standard deviation and range of scores. Also, report on an aspect of the strong (or weak) fit to the normal distribution.

Name _____   **Date** _____

1. Determine the fit to the normal curve for "Respondent's income. (Rincom98)"   Use the worksheet on the following page to make your assessment.

Interpretation of results:

Codebook information		Statistics	
Variable name		Mean	
Variable label		SD	
Minimum		Variance	
Maximum		Range	
Metric		Valid cases	
Level of Measurement			

Class intervals						Distribution	
Continuous z-score		Continuous raw score		Discrete raw score		% of cases per interval	
Lower	Upper	Lower	Upper	Lower	Upper	Observed	Expected
-4	-3						0
-3	-2						2.1
-2	-1						13.6
-1	0						34.1
0	1						34.1
1	2						13.6
2	3						2.1
3	4						0

Name _____   **Date** _____

2.   Determine the fit to the normal curve for "How often Americans read the newspaper (News)"   Use the worksheet on the following page to make your assessment.

Interpretation of results:

Codebook information		Statistics	
Variable name		Mean	
Variable label		SD	
Minimum		Variance	
Maximum		Range	
Metric		Valid cases	
Level of Measurement			

Class intervals						Distribution	
Continuous z-score		Continuous raw score		Discrete raw score		% of cases per interval	
Lower	Upper	Lower	Upper	Lower	Upper	Observed	Expected
-4	-3						0
-3	-2						2.1
-2	-1						13.6
-1	0						34.1
0	1						34.1
1	2						13.6
2	3						2.1
3	4						0

Name _____   **Date** _____

3. Determine the fit to the normal curve for "How often Americans have had sex in the past year (sexfreq)" Use the worksheet on the following page to make your assessment.

Interpretation of results:

Codebook information		Statistics	
Variable name		Mean	
Variable label		SD	
Minimum		Variance	
Maximum		Range	
Metric		Valid cases	
Level of Measurement			

Class intervals						Distribution	
Continuous z-score		Continuous raw score		Discrete raw score		% of cases per interval	
Lower	Upper	Lower	Upper	Lower	Upper	Observed	Expected
-4	-3						0
-3	-2						2.1
-2	-1						13.6
-1	0						34.1
0	1						34.1
1	2						13.6
2	3						2.1
3	4						0

Name _____   **Date** _____

4.   Determine the fit to the normal curve for "How often Americans pray (Pray)" Use the worksheet on the following page to make your assessment.

Interpretation of results:

Codebook information		Statistics	
Variable name		Mean	
Variable label		SD	
Minimum		Variance	
Maximum		Range	
Metric		Valid cases	
Level of Measurement			

Class intervals						Distribution	
Continuous z-score		Continuous raw score		Discrete raw score		% of cases per interval	
Lower	Upper	Lower	Upper	Lower	Upper	Observed	Expected
-4	-3						0
-3	-2						2.1
-2	-1						13.6
-1	0						34.1
0	1						34.1
1	2						13.6
2	3						2.1
3	4						0

Name _____   **Date** _____

Compare the frequency distribution of a standardized score with the raw scores from question 4. Find and circle the equivalent parts of the frequency distribution for x=2 and z=??.

5. Frequency distribution for Pray.

6. Frequency distribution for Zpray. Zpray is a new variable that will be located as the last variable in the dataset.

Name _____　　　　**Date** _____

7. Use Fox's Statistics calculator to convert the raw scores for praying (1 to 6) into z-scores. Use the mean and SC which you already have from question 4.

8. Draw a curve showing the approximate shape of the distribution of how often Americans pray with the z-scores and raw scores labeled on the graph.

VARIABILITY: SKEWNESS AND KURTOSIS

INTRODUCTION

In Chapter 6 we looked in great detail at the standard deviation using z-scores to assess whether a distribution is a "normal" distribution. In most instances though you're going to want to know how to quickly assess the shape of a distribution and then move to interpret the appropriate statistics: mean (or median) and standard deviation (or range). In this chapter you will:

1.   look again at skewness; and
2.   examine kurtosis as another aspect of a distribution.

Measures of distribution

The figure below shows a symmetric (normal) distribution, a positive (or right-tailed) skew, and a negative (or left-tailed) skew. We used the skewness statistic in Chapter 5 to determine whether or not the mean or median was the most appropriate measure of central tendency. If skewness is over 2 in magnitude the mean and standard deviation are biased and we use the median and range as measures of central tendency and dispersion.

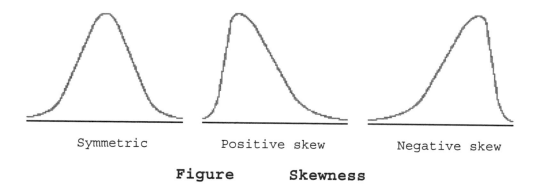

Symmetric   Positive skew   Negative skew

Figure   Skewness

A second measure of symmetry is kurtosis. The figure shows that distributions can be peaked (leptokurtic) or flat (platykurtic). An Australian named these terms as lepto (+ values) after two kangaroos lepping, and platy (- values) after the Australian platypus. He called the symmetric (normal curve) a mesokurtic distribution with a kurtosis of zero (0).

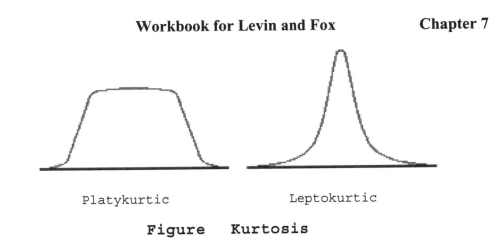

Platykurtic   Leptokurtic

Figure   Kurtosis

Looking at the platykurtic distribution, the scores may fall a large distance from the mean and we would expect a larger standard deviation. With a leptokurtic distribution, the scores fall close to the mean and we'd have a relatively small standard deviation.

If you were to take an exam, what kind of skewness and kurtosis would you like to have? I think I'd like one with a negative skew and leptokurtosis. That is, the exam would have high scores and most people would score close to the high average. Compare this to a positive skew and leptokurtosis and you'd find a low average and most people scored close to it.

Kurtosis is measured by a dimensionless number that is similar to skewness which is called a coefficient of kurtosis.

$$kurtosis = \frac{1}{N} \sum_{j=1}^{N} \frac{\left(x_j - \bar{x} \right)^4}{\sigma_x^4}$$

Knowing that kurtosis is a function of the mean and standard deviation we can also make a quick gauge of the shape of the graph by comparing the relative size of the standard deviation to the size of the mean. In doing this, we will get an idea of whether a standard deviation is large or small relative to the mean.

DATA ANALYSIS EXAMPLE

Research problem: Describe the distribution of students' political beliefs (V167).

Codebook information: Use the codebook to get the basic information about the scale. Note that the scale is a Likert scale which ranges from 1 "Very conservative" to 6 "Radical." For purposes of our analysis we will treat this variable as if it is an interval level variable so that we can calculate a mean and standard deviation.

101

Computer analysis: Use the FREQUENCIES procedure to calculate measures of central tendency, dispersion, and distribution.   Click the boxes as shown below.

Results: Looking first at skewness, .375, we find a small positive number which indicates the distribution is approximately symmetric. Next, the kurtosis of .185 is a small positive value or a mesokurtic distribution. Thus, we would describe the distribution of political beliefs of students as having a fully normal distribution (no skew and no kurtosis).

Statistics

V167 902C12 :R'POL BLF RADCL		
N	Valid	2989
	Missing	1992
Mean		3.18
Median		3.00
Std. Deviation		1.13
Skewness		.375
Std. Error of Skewness		.045
Kurtosis		.185
Std. Error of Kurtosis		.090
Range		5

Summary interpretation: We used survey data from the Monitoring the Future Study (1990 and 1999) to assess the distribution of students' political beliefs. The question used a Likert scale varying from very conservative to radical beliefs. We found a fully normal distribution (skewness =0.4; kurtosis =0.2). With a normal distribution, the mean value is an appropriate measure of the "average." The survey suggests that a typical student would describe him or herself as having moderate political beliefs (mean=3.2). The standard deviation of 1.1 is of moderate size so that we find most students falling between conservative and liberal.

Key terms

Leptokurtic
Kurtosis
Mesokurtic
Platykurtic

1.   Use the Monitoring the Future study to examine the dispersion of the number of traffic tickets (V197).

Codebook information (variable name, min, max, level of measurement, etc.)

Descriptive statistics

Mean = _____   Median = _____

Skewness = _____   Kurtosis = _____

Standard deviation = _____   Range = _____

Draw a picture of the distribution

Interpretation of results:

Name _____ Date _____

2. Use the Monitoring the Future study to examine the dispersion of satisfaction with personal safety (V1643).

Codebook information (variable name, min, max, level of measurement, etc.)

Descriptive statistics

Mean = _____ Median = _____

Skewness = _____ Kurtosis = _____

Standard deviation = _____ Range = _____

Draw a picture of the distribution

Interpretation of results:

Name _____   **Date** _____

3.   Use the Monitoring the Future study to examine the dispersion of the risk of trying marijuana once or twice (V1767).

Codebook information (variable name, min, max, level of measurement, etc.)

Descriptive statistics

Mean = _____   Median = _____

Skewness = _____   Kurtosis = _____

Standard deviation = _____   Range = _____

Draw a picture of the distribution

Interpretation of results:

Name _____   **Date** _____

4.   Use the Monitoring the Future study to examine a variable of your choice. It should be an interval level variable (or one where you can make this assumption).

Codebook information (variable name, min, max, level of measurement, etc.)

Descriptive statistics

Mean = _____   Median = _____

Skewness = _____   Kurtosis = _____

Standard deviation = _____   Range = _____

Draw a picture of the distribution

Interpretation of results:

CONFIDENCE INTERVALS

INTRODUCTION

Researchers very often would like to draw conclusions about large populations using information from a sample. You've undoubtedly seen the end product of the calculation of a confidence interval whether it was published in a news paper or in a government publication. For example, a study may find that "79 percent of Americans favor the death penalty for murderers and this result is accurate within 4 percentage points." Or, you could be reading the results from the *National Crime Victimization Survey* which reports that, in 1999, U.S. residents age 12 or older experienced approximately 28.8 million crimes: 74% (21.2 million) were property crimes, and 25% (7.4 million) were crimes of violence, and 1% were personal thefts (NCVS, 2000).

Researchers use statistics derived from samples to make two kinds of estimates about population parameters: point and interval estimates. A point estimate is a single number which is presented as a best guess for the parameter. An interval estimate is a range of values in which we can state with a degree of confidence that we believe we have identified the parameter. There are several kinds of population parameters. This chapter focuses on confidence intervals of means and proportions.

In Levin and Fox, Chapter 6 introduces the concept of the sampling distribution of means. We know, because of sampling variability, that the sample statistic may differ from the population parameter. That is, a researcher expects to make some error in estimating a population parameter when using a sample. As social science researchers we would like to be able to say what the population parameter is while allowing for some error. Researchers will typically give a range of values in which they expect the parameter to fall. The essential question comes down to what is the size of the interval? If the range is too small we will be wrong in stating that we have included the parameter. If it is too large, we may not be saying much about the parameter. The concept of a confidence interval and the procedures for estimating it assist us in identifying an appropriate size.

Confidence intervals

We use the standard error to establish the range of interval estimates. The range of values constructed about the **point estimate** (the mean) is described as the **confidence interval**. The **precision** of the estimate of an interval is the size of the interval. The **level of confidence** in the estimate refers to the probability that the estimate will contain the population parameter. Assuming that sampling errors of the mean are normally distributed, we use the area under the normal curve to estimate the population parameter. The probability of being wrong is called **alpha** (α= 1- confidence level). Social science researchers, by convention, choose either a 90%, 95% or 99% confidence interval. Using a 95% confidence interval means that alpha is 5%. Another way to say this is that a researcher runs the chance of being wrong 5 times in 100 in saying that a confidence interval contains the population parameter.

The formula for confidence intervals for means is below:

$$confidence\ interval = \mu \pm z\,\frac{\sigma}{\sqrt{N}}$$

The items in the above formula have been used in Chapters 4, 5, and 6. The mean and standard deviation of the mean are information that we get by drawing a sample from a population. Looking at the N in the formula, notice that the precision of an estimate of a parameter would increase if N was larger. Also, the size of the interval will depend on the level of confidence that is chosen because z-scores get larger for greater levels of confidence.

Can we use the above formula to calculate a confidence interval for the American population using sample data from the National Opinion Survey on Crime and Justice, the Monitoring the Future Study, or the General Social Survey? No. These are sample surveys and the above formula requires a *population* standard deviation. However, we can estimate the standard error of the mean using the *sample* standard deviation in place of the *population* standard deviation, and we can use a *t*-distribution instead of a *z*-distribution. The t-distribution takes variations in z-scores by accounting for sample sizes. Go to a t-scores table in Appendix C of Levin and Fox. The t and z-scores look very much the same for large samples (N > 120). As the sample size (N) increases, the t-distribution begins to look like the normal distribution of z-scores. This may sound complicated but it really is not. The revised formula is below:

$$confidence\ interval = \bar{x} \pm t\,\frac{s}{\sqrt{N-1}}$$

What decisions do we have using data in this workbook? Since we will use the data from the NOSCJ, MTF and the GSS, we do not have an opportunity to increase the N (we're using their data; we don't want to do another study). Nonetheless, we will select a level of confidence. The mathematics looks complicated but confidence intervals are quite simple to explain to a non-statistical person once the results are calculated.

DATA ANALYSIS EXAMPLE 1

Research problem: Calculate an interval estimate of the number of hours per data that Americans watch television. We will use the General Social Survey to make a 95% confidence interval estimate of the population parameter for television viewing for **all** American adults in the United States in 1998.

Codebook information: Use the codebook to get basic information on the level of measurement for the variable (TVHOURS). The codebook simply tells us that the variable is recorded as hours per day with "Don't Know (98)," "Refused (99)," and "Question not Asked (−1)" excluded as missing values. We would have to run a frequency distribution to obtain the minimum and maximum from the sample survey. With this kind of question, we should state the the theoretical minimum and maximum number of hours. That the minimum would be 0 and the maximum would be 24 hours. In order to calculate a confidence interval we will treat this an interval level variable with a metric of 1 hour per day.

Calculating a confidence interval: SPSS for windows calculates confidence intervals for single variables where you may select any level of confidence. By convention, we will most often use the 95 percent confidence interval, sometimes 99, and less often the 90 percent interval.

There are several ways to get SPSS to calculate a confidence interval. Let's use the ONE SAMPLE T TEST in which we will set the options 90, 95, and then 99 percent. To get this information, click on ANALYZE, move down to COMPARE MEANS, and then select the ONE SAMPLE T-TEST.

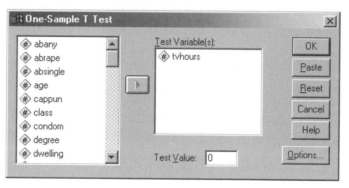

Our test variable from above is "TVHOURS." By default, a 95% confidence interval will be generated. Click on "Options" to change it to 90 and then 99 to complete the exercises.

Depending upon the statistical program (and the version of SPSS), some programs give descriptive information such as the mean and standard deviation. We will need to look for the appropriate parts that we wish to use in our interpretation.

One-Sample Statistics

	N	Mean	Std. Deviation	Std. Error Mean
TVHOURS Hours per day watching tv	2337	2.86	2.247	.046

One-Sample Test

	Test Value = 0					
					95% Confidence Interval the Difference	
	t	df	Sig. (2-tailed)	Mean Difference	Lower	Upper
TVHOURS Hours per day watching tv	61.497	2336	.000	2.86	2.77	2.95

We see that 2337 persons answered the question. The mean score is reported as 2.86 with a standard deviation of 2.247. We are not overly interested in this part of the output as we are looking for the "interval" estimate.

The one-sample t-test shows the confidence interval. Note that it states the level of confidence is 95%. You can adjust this to any level. The right side of the output shows the lower and upper limits as 2.77 and 2.95.   The width of the interval (potential size of error) is not provided but it can easily be determined using a hand calculation to see the size of the confidence interval (2.95 - 2.77 = .18 hours per day). It is always a good idea to look back into a codebook to determine what these values mean so that we can provide a summary of these results.

Interpretation: The General Social Survey (1998) asked adult Americans about their television viewing habits. A 95 percent confidence interval was calculated. We are 95% confident that the average number of hours per day of television viewing falls no lower than 2.8 hours and no higher than 3.0 hours per day. This confidence interval is based upon 2337 completed interviews of adult Americans in 1998.

DATA ANALYSIS EXAMPLE 2

Many studies include questions with "yes" or "no" type questions. This is a nominal level variable with two categories. A confidence interval can be used to estimate the percentage of responses. Levin and Fox, in Chapter 6, discuss the formula for confidence intervals using proportions.

Research problem: Calculate an interval estimate of percentage of students in American High Schools that have ever had alcoholic beverages (v103). We will use the Monitoring the Future Study to make a 95% confidence interval estimate of the population parameter for **all** American students in grade 12 in the United States in 1990 and 2000.

Codebook information: Note that no=1 and yes = 2. This is a nominal level variable with two categories. It is appropriate to calculate a confidence interval.

Computer output: The results of the analysis are shown below.

One Sample Statistics

	N	Mean	Std. Deviation	Std. Error Mean
V103 022B03 : EVER DRINK	4644	1.87	.335	.005

One-Sample Test

		t	df	Sig. (2-tailed)	Mean Difference	95% Confidence Interval of the Difference	
						Lower	Upper
V103	002B03 :EVER DRINK	380.676	4643	.000	1.87	1.86	1.88

From the codebook, a "1" means that a student does not drink and a "2" means that they do drink. A simple trick to make the 1 and 2 more intuitive is to turn them into 0 (no) and 1 (yes). We will subtract 1 from to the interval estimate.

The lower estimate is shown as 1.86 and the upper estimate is 1.88. Subtract 1.00 from each and it is now 0.86 and 0.88. Convert them to percentages by multiplying the proportions by 100. This yields a result of 86% to 88%. These are the lower and upper bounds on the percentage of American high school students that have ever had a drink of beer, wine, wine coolers and liquor. What is the interval size? The answer is 88-86 or 2 percent.

Interpretation: Based on the Monitoring the Future Study (1990 and 2000) which studies high school seniors in the United States, we are 95% confident that between 86 and 88 percent of American high school students have ever had a drink of alcohol. The question on the survey asked "Have you ever had any beer, wine, wine coolers, or liquor to drink?" The response categories were yes or no.

Another common way to present results is to report the point estimate and the amount of error (one half of the interval size goes on either side of the point estimate). In this case we would say that we estimate that about 87 percent of students have ever had a drink (look at the 1.87 in the first table). These results are accurate plus or minus 1 percent 19 times in 20 (Question: What is 19 /20?; Answer: it is another way to say 95% confidence).

When writing up the results of a confidence interval, a good summary will:
- State the source of information;
- Describe the measurement of the variable;
- Indicate the level of confidence; and
- Report either the lower and upper limits of the interval; or the point estimate and the amount of error.

Key terms

Confidence interval
Error
Interval estimate
Point estimate
Precision

Web-sites:

The Bureau of Justice Statistics : www.ojp.usdoj.gov/bjs/
    Follow the links to the National Crime Victimization Survey. You can get a description of the survey and access the full reports.

The Gallup Organization: www.gallup.com
    The Gallup organization conducts public opinion polls on a variety of social issues.

Name _____　　　　　　**Date** _____

1.　　　Using the Monitoring the Future Study, calculate 90%, 95%, and 99% confidence interval estimates on American High School students' perception of the risk of trying marijuana once or twice (V1767).

Codebook information:

Use the ONE-SAMPLE T-TEST procedure in SPSS to calculate confidence intervals. Record the information in the table below. Use hand-calculations to obtain the interval width for each group.

Confidence	Frequency	Mean	SD	Lower limit	Upper limit	Interval size
90						
95						
99						

Interpret one of the confidence intervals for the sample.

Explain what happens to the size of the interval as the level of confidence increases.

Name _____   **Date** _____

2.   Using the National Opinion Survey of Crime and Justice, calculate 90%, 95%, and 99% confidence interval estimates on the American public's opinion about whether it should be legal to sell marijuana (providing it were legal to use marijuana) (S2).

Codebook information:

Use the ONE-SAMPLE T-TEST procedure in SPSS to calculate confidence intervals. Record the information in the table below. Use hand-calculations to obtain the interval width for each group.

Confidence	Frequency	Mean	SD	Lower limit	Upper limit	Interval size
90						
95						
99						

Interpret one of the confidence intervals for the sample.

Explain what happens to the size of the interval as the level of confidence increases.

Name _____   **Date** _____

3.   Choose a variable from the General Social Survey. Calculate 90%, 95%, and 99% confidence interval estimates.

Codebook information:

Use the ONE-SAMPLE T-TEST procedure in SPSS to calculate confidence intervals. Record the information in the table below. Use hand-calculations to obtain the interval width for each group.

Confidence	Frequency	Mean	SD	Lower limit	Upper limit	Interval size
90						
95						
99						

Interpret one of the confidence intervals for the sample.

Explain what happens to the size of the interval as the level of confidence increases.

4. Use Content Select to find two research articles about public opinion on marijuana. Use these articles to compare and discuss results from high school seniors and the American public as a whole.

5. For the following data, use Fox's Statistics Calculator (Confidence intervals from raw data) to calculate a mean, standard deviation, and a 95 percent confidence interval.

   Casinos are an interesting phenomenon. We asked fifteen people exiting the casino about how much they had won or lost tonight in the casino. The results (in dollars) are reported below

   -25, -45, - 20, -30, +15, +100, -35, -25, -20, -80, -45, -30, -50, +10, -25

   Mean = _____

   SD = _____

   95% Confidencc interval = _____ to _____

   Interpretation

T-TESTS

INTRODUCTION

A t-test is used to examine the relationship between a dependent variable measured at the interval (or ratio) level and a nominal level independent variable with two categories (dichotomous). In this chapter you will:

1.   go through the steps of hypothesis testing;
2.   use t-tests to examine the form, extent, and statistical significance of bivariate relationships.

T-TESTS

Suppose you are interested in public perceptions of criminal victimization in general and sexual assault in particular. A researcher suggests that females are more likely than males to worry about getting sexually assaulted. We would like to do a statistical test to determine whether or not this statement is accurate.

Levels of Measurement

The dependent variable for our analysis is whether or not a person worries about getting sexually assaulted (W1). This is an ordinal level variable ranging from 1 (Very frequently) to (4) Never. For this example, let's assume that it is an interval level variable and that the metric is continuous ranging from never to very frequently.

The independent variable for our study is sex of the respondent (D16). This is a nominal level variable with two categories: Male (1) and Female (2).

Form

The form of the relationship in a t-test refers to the directional difference between means. In this case we suggest that the form will be such that the amount of worry about sexual assault for females will be greater than it is for males. Looking back at the scale, is a higher number more worrying or less? In fact this variable has values where a lower number means that a person would worry more. Thus we will expect that the mean for women will be a lower value than the mean for men.

Extent

The extent of the relationship in a t-test simply refers to how much of a difference there is comparing the mean for females to the mean for males.

Precision

The precision of the relationship does not apply to a t-test.

Level of significance

We will use the t-test to test whether or not there is a difference between the mean of worrying for females and males. Before proceeding we must choose a level of significance. This is a benchmark of how large the difference in means must be for us to accept that there is a statistical difference. Traditionally, social researchers use either a 95% or 99% level of confidence in results. This means that the alpha level of error will be 5% or 1%. This is usually expressed as a proportion of .05 or .01. In this example we will work using a 95% confidence level or $\alpha = .05$.

DATA ANALYSIS EXAMPLE

Research Problem: A researcher suggests that women in American worry more than men about they or someone in their family getting sexually assaulted.

Hypothesis testing: Write out the research, null and alternative hypotheses for a t-test.

Note that the null hypothesis (null means zero or none) is a statement that there is no difference between sample means. The alternative hypothesis, on the other hand, may entail three options: two-tailed, one-tail right, and one-tail left.

In a two-tailed test, we're simply looking to see whether there is a difference between the mean. We have no reason before conducting the test to expect that the differences will go one way or the other. We're just testing to see whether there is a difference. In a two-tailed test, the notation is that the first mean is simply not equal ($\neq$) to the second mean.

One tailed tests are conducted when we have a good reason to expect that one mean will be larger than the other mean. It could be that we have read an article in the literature which tells us to expect a particular relationship. Or, it could be that it seems very logical to expect a particular findings. In one tailed tests, we specify the direction where the first mean may be expected to be greater than (>) the second mean, or it will be less than (<) the second mean. Note also that we're saying the values for the t-test will be positive (greater than zero) or negative (less than zero).

In our example, we're suggesting that women worry more than men about sexual assault. Clearly, we're suggesting a direction. How are the variables coded? We need to look at the codebook to make our prediction on the direction. Sex of the respondent (D16) is coded as male (1) and female (2). Worrying about sexual assault (W1) is coded as never (4) to very frequently (1). If women, on average, are expected to worry more, what are we saying about the mean for women? We're saying that the mean for men will be larger than the mean for women ($\mu_1 > \mu_2$). It is very important to look at the codebook to see how things are coded because in this instance worrying more is a smaller value. The research, null and alternative hypotheses are shown below.

119

T-Test of difference between means

Research Hypothesis 1: Women worry more than men about they or someone in their family getting sexually assaulted.	$\alpha = .05$
Null Hypothesis: The difference in the means will equal zero.	$H_0: \mu_1 = \mu_2$
Alternative Hypothesis: The difference in means is more than zero. We specify a direction making this a one-tailed test, where men (group 1) are expected to have a larger mean than are women (group 2). This expectation is specified below using the Agreater than@ sign.	$H_1: \mu_1 > \mu_2$ (one-tailed test)

The t-test procedure in SPSS is calculated by clicking on ANALYZE, COMPARE MEANS, and the INDEPENDENT-SAMPLES T Test. Our "dependent" or "test" variable is W1. Click on W1 in the variable list and then move it to the test variable box. The "grouping" or "independent" variable is D16. Move it across and then click on "Define groups." From the codebook, we know that men are 1 and women are 2. Click on OK to execute the t-test.

The computer output is shown below. The first table shows descriptive statistics for Males (group 1) and Females (Group 2). It is a good idea to look at this table because it will show if you have entered the dependent and independent variables in the correct boxes. If it showed 1

Very frequently and 2 Somewhat freq in the group statistics then you should immediately note that you need to redo the analysis (A common error for first time users).

Group Statistics

	D16 SEX OF RESPONDENT	N	Mean	Std. Deviation	Std. Error Mean
W1 WORRY: YOU/FAMILY SEXUALLY ASSAULTED	1 Male	522	3.00	.929	.041
	2 Female	480	2.71	1.025	.047

Independent Samples Test

		Levene's Test for Equal: of Variances		t-test for Equality of Means		
		F	Sig.	t	df	Sig. (2-tailed
W1 WORRY: YOU/F MILY SEXUALLY ASSAULTED	Equal variances assumed	28.211	.000	4.724	1000	.000
	Equal variances not assumed			4.705	968.258	.000

Next, look to the lower table where you'll see two types of t-tests: Equal variances and unequal variances. Thinking back to Chapter 5, what is variance? It's related to standard deviations. In essence, the computer is looking to see whether the variation in male scores is the same (equal) to the variation for female scores. Look at the standard deviations in this example (.93 male; 1.03 female). Are they about the same? They look close, but the Levene's F-test tells us that the variation (s^2) for men and women is really different. Using an alpha level of .05, we look to the F-ratio and make a decision about which t-test to read. In this case, F=28.2, p<.05. If the probability is less than .05 we use the unequal test. If the probability is greater than .05 then we use an equal test. Here the Levene's test is significant so that we use the unequal t-test (Equal variances not assumed). The computer prints both so that the researcher can do the analysis in one step.

The t-value is 4.705. A two-tailed probability is printed by default. If you're doing a two-tailed test, you would simply take the significance level as the probability of the result.

What kind of test did we hypothesize? A one tailed positive (right-tailed) test! Is the t-test value positive? 4.705 is a positive number. If it was –4.949 we would stop and say that we failed to reject the null. To finish up, we simply divide the printed significant by two.

Two-tailed significant / 2 = one-tailed signficance;   .000/2 = .000

121

The results of your research should be written into a summary notation as follows:

t (df) = value, p-level (either p<.05 or p>.05)

The degrees of freedom for the test are printed in the output. Round the degrees of freedom to the nearest whole number.

In this example the result of the t-test is: t (968) = 4.71, p < .05.

We have found a significant difference in the means for men and women. We reject the null hypothesis that men and women worry equally about whether they or someone in their family is going to be sexually assaulted.   We now need to go back to the means and interpret the form and extent of the difference.

The descriptive statistics table reports the means as: Male = 3.00 and Female= 2.71. The mean for males is a larger number which suggests than men worry less than women about sexual assault of a family member. How much less? Simply subtract 2.71 – 3.00 to get -.29 units. The extent of the difference is .29 units of the metric which we will call .29 units of worry. We're ready to write up our summary of the entire analysis.

Interpretation:
An analysis of the 1995 National Opinion Survey of Crime and Justice shows that women are more likely than men to worry about they or someone in their family getting sexually assaulted. Response categories on this question were never (4), seldom (3), somewhat frequently (2) and very frequently (1). We used an F-test (F= 28.2, p<.05) to select an unequal variance t-test. The difference in means in significant (t (968)= 4.71, p<.05). The form of the relationship is that women (M=2.71) are more likely than men (M=3.00) to worry about sexual assault of themselves or a family member. The extent of the difference is .29 units of worry. This difference in means is large enough that we reject the null hypothesis of no differences in means about worry at a .05 level of significance. However, while we have found a *significant* difference between men and women, this is not a *substantively* large difference in the means. We find that the average for women and men is such that both sexes say they "seldom" worry about sexual assault of themselves or a family member.

When writing up the results of a t-test, a good summary will:
- State the source of information;
- Describe the measurement of the dependent variable and state which groups are being compared;
- Indicate the level of confidence;
- State the decision on the null hypothesis as reject or fail to reject; and
- Discuss the form and extent of the difference (when the null hypothesis is rejected).

KEY TERMS

Alternative hypothesis
equal variances assumed
equal variances not assumed
Levine's F-test
Null hypothesis
One-tailed test (right or left)
Research hypothesis
Significance
t-test
Two-tailed test

Name _____   **Date** _____

1. *Research Problems:* Use the Monitoring the future study to test the following hypothesis:

Research hypothesis: There will be a difference in marijuana use comparing students in 1990 to students in 2000. (V115 and Year)

Write out the null and alternative hypothesis

Which t-test? Explain your choice

The results:

Write out a brief interpretation

2.   *Research Problems:* Use the Monitoring the future study to test a hypothesis:

Choose a nominal level 2-N independent variable and an appropriate dependent variable.

Write out a research, null, and alternative hypothesis

Which t-test? Explain your choice

The results:

Write out a brief interpretation

Name _____   Date _____

3.   Research Problems: Use the General Social Survey, 1998.

Research hypothesis: Males are more likely than females to say that it is okay to have extra-
                                    marital sex. (Xmarsex and sex)

Write out the null and alternative hypothesis

Which t-test? Explain your choice

The results:

Write out a brief interpretation

Name _____   Date _____

4.   Research Problems: Use the General Social Survey, 1998.

Choose a nominal level 2-N independent variable and an appropriate dependent variable.

Write out the research, null, and alternative hypothesis

Which t-test? Explain your choice

The results:

Write out a brief interpretation

Name _____   **Date** _____

Use Fox's Statistics Calculator to calculate t-tests for the following problems.

5. A researcher is interested in the effect of stress on cigarette smoking. Sixteen subjects (independent samples) who smoke cigarettes were selected an were asked to compose an essay on the meaning of life. Eight of them composed their essays while seated in an uncomfortable chair, and were given very negative feedback on their essay quality (high stress condition). The other eight composed their essays in comfort and were given positive feedback (low stress condition). All subjects were then taken to a room where smoking was allowed (and cigarettes were supplied for those persons who didn't have any) and were asked to wait for an hour before continuing the experiment. The number of cigarettes smoked by people in each group was recorded and is presented below. The null hypothesis is that there will be no difference in cigarette consumption between people in the two different stress conditions.

> High stress: 2, 2, 4, 5, 3, 1, 4, 3
> Low stress: 1, 3, 2, 2, 4, 2, 1, 1

    a.   Write out an alternative hypothesis.

    b.   What is the mean number of cigarettes smoked for the high stress sample? _____

                … for the low stress sample? _____

    c.   What are the standard deviations for each group? SD (High) = _____

                …. SD (Low) = _____

    d.   Calculate the standard error of the difference between the means. _____

    e.   Calculate the t-ratio. _____
    f.   Determine the degrees of freedom. _____
    g.   Assume an alpha of .05. What is the critical score or ratio? _____

    h.   Do you reject or fail to reject the null hypothesis? _____
    i.   Write an interpretation of the results.

Name _____   **Date** _____

6. Dr. Williams develops an hypothesis. She feels that after fours years of college that a persons self-perception should be different. Dr. Williams randomly selects 6 students just starting college and administers an Opinion of Self Perception Test (OSPT). Four years later, she administers the OSPT to these same students. The results are:

Year 1	Year 4
13	18
10	15
15	12
11	20
8	21
12	19

a. Are these samples related? Explain.

b. What is the null hypothesis?

c. What is the alternative hypothesis?

d. What is the standard deviation of the distribution of difference scores? _____

e. What is the standard error of the mean difference? _____

f. Assume an alpha of .05. What is the critical t-value? _____

g. What is the value of the t-test? _____

h. What is Dr. Williams' research decision?

ANALYSIS OF VARIANCE (ANOVA)

INTRODUCTION

Males versus females, parents versus children, and delinquent versus non-delinquent are some of the many two-sample comparisons that we may wish to make in understanding social behavior. However, group variation goes beyond simple dichotomies.

Researchers will often need to make comparisons of three or more samples or groups. For example, you may wish to compare people of different marital status (Married, Widowed, Single, Divorced or Separated), race (Black, White, Hispanic, Other) or of different geographical regions (Northeast, Northcentral, South, and West) to determine whether an independent variable is statistically related to a dependent variable such as attitudes toward marijuana use.

This chapter introduces you to analysis of variance (ANOVA) to test the situation where you have an interval (or ratio) level dependent variable and a nominal level independent variable with three or more groups. The independent variable, in fact, may actually be measured at a higher level of measurement (ordinal, interval, or ratio) but ANOVA simply treats it as a nominal variable.

You may be wondering why we don't just do a series of t-tests to compare the means in the groups. The t-test assumes that independent samples are drawn from a population. If we make more than one comparison, the groups would not be from independent samples. Thus, we need a more sophisticated test.

ANALYSIS OF VARIANCE

This chapter will use the one-way analysis of variance procedure (ONE-WAY ANOVA). The ONE-WAY procedure is the simplest type of ANOVA for understanding bivariate relationships.

Form

Unlike a t-test, where there is just one comparison, an ANOVA may have multiple groups for comparison. The form of the relationship in ONEWAY is a description of the pattern of differences in the means.

Extent

The extent of the relationship in an ANOVA is identical to that of a t-test where you describe the magnitude of differences in the means.

Precision

The precision of an ANOVA refers to the strength of association of the variables. A statistic called eta-squared (η^2) is used to measure how well we are able to explain variation in the dependent variable given knowledge of an independent variable. The formula is shown below. You will calculate this statistic by hand in this lab.

$$\eta^2 = \frac{SS_{between}}{SS_{total}} = \frac{\text{Explained variance}}{\text{Total variance}}$$

Eta-squared is interpreted as a proportion of explained variance. Eta-squared ranges from 0 to 1. A higher proportion indicates a higher degree of association between the variables. We will multiple the proportion by 100 to report a percentage of explained variation. In social science research it is not unusual to have a statistically significant relationship and a very low proportion of explained variance (for example, less than .04 or 4 percent of the variance).

Level of significance

We will use $\alpha = .05$ as the criterion for significance in the example.

DATA ANALYSIS EXAMPLE

Research Problem: Is there a statistical relationship between how often a person spends an evening in a bar and their marital status?

We will use a one-way analysis of variance test to examine this question using a sample of Americans from the 1998 General Social Survey.

Codebook information: Use the codebook to get basic information about each variable. We will assume that the scale for evenings in a bar is an interval level variable. An examination of the frequency distribution for SOCBAR shows that it approximates a normal distribution (M=5.6, Skewness= -.98). The following table identifies the characteristics of each variable:

Variable(s) and value(s)				
Dependent variable			**Independent variable**	
Variable name	SOCBAR		Variable name	D4
Variable label	Spend an evening in a bar		Variable label	Marital status
Minimum category (value)	1= Almost daily		Minimum Category (value)	1= Married
Maximum category (value)	7= Never		Maximum Category (value)	5= Never married
Level of measurement	assume interval		Level of measurement	nominal
Metric	1 unit on scale		Metric	n.a.

Hypothesis: Write out a research, null and alternative hypothesis for the research problem.

ONEWAY Analysis of Variance

Research Hypothesis:
        Americans likelihood of spending an evening in a bar will
        be related to their marital status.
	$\alpha = .05$

Null Hypothesis: None of the group means will differ from the total (or grand) mean.	$H_0: \mu_i \ldots \mu_j = \mu_{total}$

Alternative Hypothesis:	$H_1 : \mu_i ... \mu_j \neq \mu_{total}$
At least one of the group means on frequenting time in a bar will differ from the total (or grand) mean.	(two-tailed test)

The oneway analysis of variance procedure provides an omnibus test, the F-ratio, of whether or not at least one of the means ($\mu_i ... \mu_j$) differs from the total mean (μ_{total}). The F-ratio and its derivation is discussed in greater detail in Chapter 8 of Levin and Fox.

To Generate the basic output, select ANALYZE, COMPARE MEANS, and then One-Way ANOVA. The basic dialogue box is shown below. The dependent variable is entered into the dependent list and the independent variable is entered as a "factor." We also need to select out "options" and "post hoc" test(s). In options, check "descriptive" in the statistics box. In Post Hoc, select the "Scheffe" test. A large variety of range tests are available but this one is the most commonly used test. An advanced course in ANOVA is required to explain the nuances for each range test.

Computer output (one way analysis of variance):

ANOVA

SOCBAR Spend evning at bar

	Sum of Squares	df	Mean Square	F	Sig.
Between Groups	502.328	4	125.582	47.0257	.000
Within Groups	4932.199	1856	2.657		
Total	5434.527	1860			

The F-ratio is printed in the output of the Summary ANOVA table as 47.257. A variety of notations to summarize the F-ratio are used in the literature. Most social science publications use the format of the American Psychological Association (APA). It is important to use a consistent notation reporting statistics, the degrees of freedom, a rounded-off value, and the probability level:

General form: F (df-between, df-within) = value, p-level (p<.05, or p>.05).

In our example: $F (4, 1856) = 47.3, p<.05$

Interpretation of F-Ratio:

Our analysis shows that there is a statistically significant relationship between the number of evenings out in a bar and a person=s marital status. ($F (4, 1856) = 47.3, p<.05$)

Since there is a significant relationship, we may proceed to calculate eta-squared and we may conduct multiple range tests. The F-ratio does not tell us which means differ from each other, nor does it tell us by how much they differ. We need to conduct additional "post hoc" analysis of these data to determine where the differences exist.

Calculating η^2

$\eta^2 = 502.3/ 5434.5 = .092$ or 9.2%

Eta-squared is not directly printed in the SPSS output. Recall that eta-squared is calculated by taking the sum of squares between and dividing it by the sum of squares total. We find that the precision of this relationship is low to moderate in size. We are able to explain about 9.2 percent of the variation in evenings out in a bar if we know a person=s marital status.

Multiple range tests

Since the F-ratio is significant (we reject the null hypothesis that each of the group means is equal to the total mean) we proceed to conduct multiple comparisons of the means. If the F-ratio was not significant we would not conduct these tests. There are a wide variety of range tests but the most commonly used test is the Scheffe test. We checked Scheffe as an option for post hoc comparisons of means.

Multiple Comparisons

Dependent Variable: SOCBAR   Spend evening at bar

Scheffe

(I) MARITAL Marital sta	(J) MARITAL Marital sta	Mean Difference (I-	Std. Error	Sig.	95% Confidence Interval	
					Lower Bound	Upper Bound
1 MARRIED	2 WIDOWED	-.38	.136	.105	-.80	.04
	3 DIVORCED	.60	.109	.000	.27	.94
	4 SEPARATED	.41	.223	.486	-.27	1.10
	5 NEVER MARRIED	1.16	.095	.000	.87	1.45
2 WIDOWED	1 MARRIED	.38	.136	.105	-.04	.80
	3 DIVORCED	.98	.157	.000	.50	1.46
	4 SEPARATED	.79	.249	.040	.02	1.56
	5 NEVER MARRIED	1.54	.147	.000	1.08	1.99
3 DIVORCED	1 MARRIED	-.60	.109	.000	-.94	-.27
	2 WIDOWED	-.98	.157	.000	-1.46	-.50
	4 SEPARATED	-.19	.236	.956	-.92	.54
	5 NEVER MARRIED	.55	.123	.000	.17	.93
4 SEPARATED	1 MARRIED	-.41	.223	.486	-1.10	.27
	2 WIDOWED	-.79	.249	.040	-1.56	-.02
	3 DIVORCED	.19	.236	.956	-.54	.92
	5 NEVER MARRIED	.75	.230	.033	.04	1.45
5 NEVER MARRIED	1 MARRIED	-1.16	.095	.000	-1.45	-.87
	2 WIDOWED	-1.54	.147	.000	-1.99	-1.08
	3 DIVORCED	-.55	.123	.000	-.93	-.17
	4 SEPARATED	-.75	.230	.033	-1.45	-.04

'The mean difference is significant at the .05 level.

A range test is interpreted like a t-test where two groups are compared to each other. Unfortunately SPSS does not provide a conventional summary table of results. The usual procedure is to arrange the means from lowest to highest and then to calculate whether or not they are significantly different from each other. Fortunately, though, the computer program does makes all of these comparisons.

A conventional table can be rebuilt based on the following steps:

1) Using the "Descriptives," arrange the means from the lowest to the highest value. The "Descriptives" were obtained by checking its box in "Options."
1) Record the N's for each group.
3) Place an asterisk beside comparisons where the mean difference in values is significant at _ = .05.
1) Draw –'s on the diagonal where variables are compared to themselves (e.g. 2 to 2); and
1) By APA convention, only the upper half of the multiple range table is completed.

Descriptives

SOCBAR Spend evening at bar

		N	Mean	Std. Deviati	Std. Errc	95% Confidence Interval Mean		Minimum	Maximum
						Lower Bounc	Upper Bounc		
1	MARRIED	908	5.96	1.436	.048	5.86	6.05	1	7
2	WIDOWED	171	6.33	1.443	.110	6.12	6.55	1	7
3	DIVORCED	295	5.35	1.778	.104	5.15	5.56	1	7
4	SEPARATED	57	5.54	1.774	.235	5.07	6.01	2	7
5	NEVER MARRIED	430	4.80	1.932	.093	4.61	4.98	1	7
Total		1861	5.62	1.709	.040	5.54	5.69	1	7

Let's take a moment to look at the means in the descriptives table. What is the average number of times for married people spending an evening in the bar? The computer output shows a mean of 5.96. We need to go back to our codebook for a moment. An M=5.96 is closest to the category of 6 which means that married persons averaged about once per year. Have a look in the codebook to interpret the mean for each of the other group's mean scores.

Arrange these mean scores from lowest to highest so that we can construct the multiple range test table. The lowest mean score is 4.80 for never married, followed by 5.35 for divorced, and so on. Record the group and label, the group N, and the mean value in the multiple range test table.

Multiple Range test							
Group/Label	N	Mean (smallest to largest)	5	3	4	1	2
5 Never married	430	4.80	--	*	*	*	*
3 Divorced	295	5.35		--		*	*
4 Separated	57	5.54			--		*
1 Married	908	5.96				--	
2 Widowed	171	6.33					--
					Significant differences * = p< .05		

Next, we want to find out which groups are significantly different from each other. Working in the rows in the new table, we will start with never married. Look back at never married labeled as multiple comparisons to see if there were any asterisks in this blocking. Do you see any? Yes, there are asterisks beside every group in this first comparison. Mark an asterisk in the new table in row 1 for each group. Next, move to Divorced in row 2. Look at divorced in the computer output. Are there any asterisks? Yes; Married and Never Married. Place an asterisk under # 1 for married. We skip the asterisk for Divorced and Never married because it could go on the lower side of the matrix. By convention only the upper half of the table is completed. We still know that Divorced and Never Married are different because of the asterisk in the first row. Continue to the next row and complete the table. Remember that only the upper half of the table is completed.

Interpretation of Multiple Range tests:

Each asterisk in the output refers to a significant difference at the .05 level between two means. For example, looking at never married persons in the top line and looking across we see that never married persons are significantly different than every other group. This means that they are significantly more likely than every other group to spend an evening in the bar. The extent of the differences in means actually tells us how much more likely they are to go to the bar as well.

Each blank space in the table tells us that there are no significant differences between groups. For example, divorced and separated people have different means (5.35 and 5.54) but the extent of the difference is not large enough to be significantly different. While this might look like a large difference, it could also be that there are too few separated persons in the sample for us to be confident that this is a reliable difference. The post hoc test takes the sample sizes into account as it calculates the significance of differences. A computer program will use its bank of calculations of Scheffe tables and tell us whether a difference in means is significant at the .05 level.

There are a large number of comparisons that are possible in this multiple range table. You should familiarize yourself with reading and drawing multiple range tables (when a table is appropriate). A full interpretation involves drawing out some of the comparisons to suggest why the analysis is important.

Summary interpretation:

We use the 1998 General Social Survey to test whether bar attendance varies by marital status. The scale on evenings out in a bar ranges from almost daily (1) to never (7). Marital status was measured as married, widowed, divorced, separated, and never married. Using a One-way ANOVA, we reject the null hypothesis that the means were equal based on $F_{(4, 1856)} = 47.3$, $p < .05$. A Scheffe range test, shown in the table above, indicates that single persons in America are somewhat more likely than all other groups to spend an evening in the bar. Single persons averaged between once a month and several times a year (M=4.8). Divorced and separated persons reported averages corresponding with several times a year. Married and widowed persons reported the highest average scores on the scale so that their averages were about once per year.

These differences between groups as shown in the multiple range table are significant but these results should be viewed with some caution. When we know a persons marital status we are only able to explain a low to moderate amount of the variation in evenings out at a bar. ($\eta^2 = 9.2\%$).

When writing up the results of an ANOVA test, a good summary will:

- State the source of information;
- Describe the measurement of the dependent variable and state which groups are being compared;
- Indicate the level of confidence;
- State the decision on the null hypothesis as reject or fail to reject.
- A multiple range table should be included if there are a large number of groups;
- Discuss the form and extent of differences when the null hypothesis is rejected; and
- Report the overall precision of the test (η^2).

KEY TERMS

American Psychological Association: APA format
ANOVA
ANOVA summary table
Descriptives
ETA
ETA-SQUARED
F-Ratio
Sum of squares
Mean Square
Multiple range test
One-way
Post hoc test
Scheffe statistic

Name _____   **Date** _____

Research Problems: Use a One-way analysis of variance to test the following hypotheses:

Research hypothesis 1.   Use the General Social Survey to test if religiosity (Feelrel) is statistically related to marital status (Marital).

Write out the null and alternative hypotheses

Summary ANOVA Table

	SS	df	MS	F	Sig	Eta-squared
Between						
Within						
Total						

Is the F-Ratio significant?

Post-hoc Table

Interpretation of results

Research Problems: Use a One-way analysis of variance to test the following hypotheses:

Research hypothesis 2.   Use the Monitoring the Future Study to test whether cocain use (V124) varies by School Region (V13).

Write out the null and alternative hypotheses

Summary ANOVA Table

	SS	df	MS	F	Sig	Eta-squared
Between						
Within						
Total						

Is the F-Ratio significant?

Post-hoc Table

Interpretation of results

Name _____   **Date** _____

Research Problems: Use a One-way analysis of variance to test the following hypotheses:

Research hypothesis 3.   Choose a drug use question from the Monitoring the Future Study to see whether it varies by interest in school (V1682).

Write out the null and alternative hypotheses

Summary ANOVA Table

	SS	df	MS	F	Sig	Eta-squared
Between						
Within						
Total						

Is the F-Ratio significant?

Post-hoc Table

Interpretation of results

Research Problems: Use Fox's Statistics Calculator to calculate an ANOVA using raw data:

Based on his own experiences in court, a prosecutor believes that some judges provide more severe penalties than others for people convicted for domestic assault and battery. A sample of five of the most recent domestic assault and battery sentences (in months) handed down by each of the three judges are shown below.

Judge #1	Judge # 2	Judge # 3
1	3	1
1	2	5
3	4	2
2	3	1
2	4	1

    a. Test the hypothesis that some judges give longer sentences than others for the same offense at (α =.05).

    b. If appropriate, construct a multiple range table. Why/Why not?

    c. Write out an overall summary.

CROSS-TABULAR ANALYSIS AND CHI-SQUARED

INTRODUCTION

In Chapters 9 and 10, you were introduced to t-tests and analysis of variance. Each of these statistical methods is powerful for testing hypotheses. While both methods are commonly used by social science researchers, you need to know that it is often difficult to meet the basic assumptions of parametric statistics: (1) normality in a population, and (2) that variables are measured at the interval or ratio level.

Researchers often will be faced with studying the relationships between variables that are nonparametric: (1) samples are not normally distributed, (2) samples are not drawn from a population, and (3) variables are measured at the nominal or ordinal level. In fact, a great deal of social science research fails to meet the assumptions of parametric statistics so that researchers must depend on a variety of nonparametric statistics to test the significance of relationships between variables.

This chapter introduces cross-tabulations for analyzing independence of two variables. Specifically, we use cross-tabulations (cross-tabs) to compare the distribution of one dependent variable across the categories of an independent variable. Both variables must be *discrete* and they usually are measured at the nominal or ordinal level.

A cross-tab usually consists of **two or more** columns and **two or more** rows. (A frequency distribution has **one** column and two or more rows.) The conventional way of building a cross-tab is for the rows to correspond with the dependent variable and the columns correspond with the independent variable. While cross-tabulations may involve two or more variables, this chapter only discusses two-way (or bi-variate) cross-tabs. The use and interpretation of multi-way cross-tabs extends beyond an introduction to statistics.

This chapter will illustrate a **two-way chi-square** test of independence. The chi-square test is perhaps the simplest application for testing the significance of bi-variate relationships when variables are measured at the nominal or ordinal level. We will demonstrate how to measure the form, extent and precision of bi-variate cross-tabular relationships.

CROSS-TABS AND THE CHI-SQUARE TEST

An important aspect of a cross-tab is its size. The convention for describing size is to state the number of rows (r) and columns (c) it contains. For example, we may examine households in the United States with guns (2 categories; yes or no) and sex (2 categories; male or female). The cross-tab will be a two by two (r x c; or 2 x 2) table. Multiplication of the number of rows by columns tells us that there will be four **cells** in the table. The size of the table is very important because many statistics, including chi-square, do not work well when the number of cells is large and the expected number of cases in some cells may be small. Levin and Fox, in Chapter 9 of their text, discuss the Yates correction of chi square for the problem of small expected frequencies. SPSS will print the Yate's correction and a warning about the percentage of cells with low expected frequencies when appropriate. Fox's Statistics Calculator shows it as well.

The conventional method for building a cross-tabulation table is to put categories of the dependent variable in the rows and the categories of the independent variable as columns. This is the general method recommended in the *Publication Manual of the American Psychological Association* which. Column percentages are calculated for each cell where the count in each cell is divided by the column total and multiplied by 100. A researcher will Apercentage down@ and Acompare across@ columns. If the dependent variable is placed on the top of the table, a row percentage should be used and comparisons will be made by comparing down the column. These kinds of tables are often used when a researcher has developed a table to "fit the page." Try to avoid making these kinds of tables in your own research since they are non-conventional and they may confuse a general reader.

Form and extent

Establishing the form of a cross-tab depends on the size of the table and the level of measurement of the variables. There are many different possible types of cross-tabs. Chi-square is considered as an appropriate statistic when both the dependent and independent variables are at the nominal level, or one of the variables is nominal and the other is ordinal. The discussion below very much simplifies the possibilities for form and extent.

2 x 2 table (row by column)

In a 2 x 2 table both variables can be considered as measured at the nominal level. Column percentages are required to make an assessment of form. The convention for stating form is to subtract the column percentage in the top left cell from the column percentage in the top right cell. The **form** refers to whether the column percentage of the top left cell is **larger or smaller** than the top left cell. The **extent** of the relationship is the **percentage difference** of the two cells.

2 x c table when the independent variable is nominal

The form in a 2 x c table when n is nominal is calculated by comparing each of the column percentages to a reference category. The reference category is determined by the researcher to meet his or her needs. For example, I live in the South of the United States. I might want to make my comparisons based on regional location using South as my reference point. Thus, comparisons would be made of all other regions to the South. The convention for form is to use the top cells of the table. The extent of the differences between cells are determined by subtracting the column percentage in each of the top cells from the column percentage in the reference cell (e.g. South). Note that the "reference" cell is the most important cell for a particular research project. As a gerontologist you might compare elderly persons to others; As a young person you might select your age group versus others; and so on. What is important to you in presenting the results of your study may differ from what is important to another person.

2 x r table when the independent variable is ordinal

The form in a 2 by r table when n is ordinal is calculated by estimating an average percentage difference across cells. To simplify the overall presentation of results the form is assumed to be uniform (increasing or decreasing equally) as you move across the length of the cross-tab. An ordinal variable may have many categories as we're trying to provide a brief summary of the results rather than force the reader to examine every cell in a table. The form and extent are assessed by taking the column percentage in the top right cell, subtracting the column percentage in the top left cell and dividing by the number of cells that we go across as we move from left to right. The **form** is positive, negative or none. The **extent** is the average percentage difference that results per cell moving across the cross-tab. For example, in a 2 x 3 table we would move across 2 cells. The extent would be the column differences divided by two (3-1=2).

r by c table when r is more than two categories and the independent variable is nominal

Lastly, in an r by c table and when r has more two categories yields several possibilities for assessing form and extent. If r is an ordinal level variable, you should focus on either the top or bottom row of the cross-tab to examine the column percentages as in a nominal level table. If r is nominal with more than 2 categories, you should choose a reference category that is considered as most important to you and report on the column percentages in that row. The objective of cross-tabular analysis is to summarize the most important features of a table rather than to report all of the cell information.

It is critical that you identify the **level of measurement** of each variable and the **number of categories** for each variable so that you may decide how best to determine the form and extent of a bi-variate cross-tabulation.

Precision

The precision of a cross-tab refers to how well you are able to improve your understanding of the dependent variable by knowing something about the independent variable.

Two statistics will be described in this chapter: Phi and the Cramer's V test. Some researchers argue that these statistics are not reliable. Others suggest that they provide a simple estimate of the precision of relationships.

Phi (Ø) is calculated as a derivative of chi-squared (χ^2) and sample size (N):

$$\phi = \sqrt{\frac{\chi^2}{N}}$$

We can interpret phi as a **proportion reduction of error** (PRE) statistic if we square it ($Ø^2$). Simply note that $Ø^2$ ranges from zero to one where a larger proportion indicates a higher level of precision. A benchmark for level of precision is: 0 to .2 is very weak; .2 to .4 is weak to moderate; .4 to .6 is moderate to strong; .6 to .8 is strong to very strong; and .8 to 1 is very strong to perfect. Most significant relationships in Criminal Justice will fall in the weak to moderate range. You may obtain phi directly from the computer output and calculate the precision by squaring it. Phi applies with 2 x 2 tables. Otherwise, use Cramer's V. We will not go into a derivation of Cramer's V. Simply consider Cramer's V as equivalent to Phi where you will square it and also interpret it as a PRE statistic.

Statistical Significance of Chi-square

Hypothesis testing in bi-variate tables tests the hypothesis that the two variables are independent of each other. The basic assumptions for the use of chi-square are:

1.   there are independent random samples,
2.   variables are measured at the nominal or ordinal level, and
3.   no expected cell frequency is less than 5.

The null hypothesis is that differences in column percentages are zero (null). The alternative is that the differences are not equal to zero. We express the null hypothesis as H_0: $\chi^2 = 0$; and the alternative as H_1: $\chi^2 \neq 0$.

We are testing the hypothesis that the chi-square is equal to zero or that the column proportions (percentages) are equal to zero. Essentially, we are looking to see whether the observed frequencies are equal to what would be expected under random conditions of chance. Chi-square is computed as:

$$\chi^2 = \Sigma \frac{(f_o - f_e)^2}{f_e}$$

where f_o = observed cell frequency; and f_e = expected cell frequency. The observed cell frequencies are what you find in your research. The expected cell frequencies are computed as:

$$f_e = \frac{(column\ marginal \times row\ marginal)}{N}$$

The marginals are the totals of the frequencies in each row and column.

To determine if the value of chi-square is significant, we must first determine the degrees of freedom. The degrees of freedom (df) is equal to the number of row minus one multiplied by the number of columns minus one. For example, in a 2 x 2 table the df is (2-1)(2-1) = 1.

As in the t and F distributions, χ^2 has a distribution determined by the degrees of freedom. If chi-square exceeds the critical value in the table it is considered as significant. The SPSS computer output prints out an estimate for the probability of obtaining a chi-square of a particular size. If the p-value is less than our alpha level (.05 or .01) we will consider the observed value to be significant.

DATA ANALYSIS EXAMPLE

Research Problem: Suppose that we want to find out whether or not there is a statistical relationship between a citizen's willingness to increase taxes to build more prisons (R13) and their stated political preference (D6). Citizen's willingness to increase taxes to build more prisons is the dependent variable and their political preference is the independent variable.

Codebook information:

The codebook shows that the question on the survey about taxes to build prisons (R13) is a nominal level variable with three categories: favor (1), oppose (2), and neither (3). Political preference on this survey is a nominal level variable with four categories: Republican (1), Democrat (2), Independent (3), and Other (4).
As in all decision-making tasks, we need to specify our hypothesis.

Hypothesis: Write out a research, null and alternative hypothesis for the research problem using an alpha level of $p < .05$.

Research Hypothesis:
      Opinions about increased taxes to build more prisons will be
      Related to political orientation.
	$\alpha = .05$

Null Hypothesis: . Opinion on taxes and political preference are independent.	$H_0: \chi^2 = 0$
Alternative Hypothesis: Opinion on taxes and political preference are not independent.	$H_1: \chi^2 \neq 0$

Note that all chi-square hypotheses will use the two-tailed notation of not equal to zero. Why? What do we know about nominal level variables? The answer is that they can't be ranked and it would be appropriate to specify a direction. Thus, an alternative hypothesis of greater than and less than zero does not apply to this statistic.

To calculate a cross-tabulation you should click on ANALYZE, DESCRIPTIVE STATISTICS, and then select CROSSTABS. The dialogue box follows:

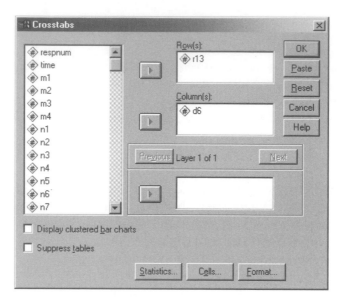

To select statistics, click on "Statistics" and check "Chi-square" and "Phi and Cramer's V." To obtain column percentages, click on "Cells" and check "Column." By default the frequency count is already checked in the cells options.

What will the computer output look like? We know that political orientation has four categories and opinions about taxes has three categories. We will get a 4 x 3 table with 12 cells. You should make this assessment before calculating the statistics. Making this assessment will also help you to prepare for calculation of form and extent.

Computer output:

The case processing summary is important since it will tell us about the number of valid cases in the cross-tabulation. We would like to use variables where fewer than 10 percent of cases are lost. The cross-tab by default removes cases where information is missing on either variable. In our example, we see that about 8 percent of cases are missing. This is an acceptable amount of missing cases.

Case Processing Summary

	Cases					
	Valid		Missing		Total	
	N	Percent	N	Percent	N	Percent
R13 FAVOR: MORE TAXES FOR PRISONS * D6 PARTY AFFILIATION	928	92.3%	77	7.7%	1005	100.0%

The cross-tab itself is shown below. Note that the independent variable is on top (columns) and the dependent variable is on the side (rows). The count and column percent (within party affiliation) are shown. The column percentages each add up to 100.

R13 FAVOR: MORE TAXES FOR PRISONS * D6 PARTY AFFILIATION Crosstabulation

			D6 PARTY AFFILIATION				
			1 Republican	2 Democrat	3 Independent	4 Other	Total
R13 FAVOR: MORE TAXES FOR PRISONS	1 Favor	Count	102	78	108	6	294
		% within D6 PARTY AFFILIATION	35.4%	28.2%	31.2%	35.3%	31.7%
	2 Oppose	Count	169	195	223	9	596
		% within D6 PARTY AFFILIATION	58.7%	70.4%	64.5%	52.9%	64.2%
	3 Neither	Count	17	4	15	2	38
		% within D6 PARTY AFFILIATION	5.9%	1.4%	4.3%	11.8%	4.1%
Total		Count	288	277	346	17	928
		% within D6 PARTY AFFILIATION	100.0%	100.0%	100.0%	100.0%	100.0%

The computer prints out several kinds of chi-square statistics. We will use the Pearson chi-square statistic, and either Phi or Cramer's V. Phi is used in 2 x 2 tables.

Our analysis shows that there is a significant relationship between public opinion about increased taxes for prisons and political preference. The chi-square is 15.4 with 6 *df* and a significance of .018. The significance meets our criterion of p<.05. The summary notation is:

$$\chi^2 \text{(df)} = \text{value, p -value (p< .05; or p> .05)}, \quad \text{or} \quad \chi^2 (6) = 15.4, \text{p<.05}$$

Note that SPSS in this cross-tab reports that there is 1 cell (8.3%) with a low expected count of less than 5. This percentage is calculated as the number of cells with low counts versus the total number of cells (1 of 12 cells; 8.3% of all cells). If this percentage of low cells exceeds 20 percent we would need to consider collapsing categories or removing some categories. Look back at the cross-tab where you'll see we have included a category of other political affiliation. There are very few people in this category. We may wish to remove it by setting it to missing. It isn't a serious problem for this table since 8.3% is less than 20 percent.

Since the relationship between opinion on taxes for prisons and political orientation is significant, we reject the null hypothesis that there is no relationship between the variables. If a relationship is statistically significant, we proceed to determine the form, extent, and precision of the relationship. Otherwise, we would simply say there is no relationship between the variables.

Chi-Square Tests

	Value	df	Asymp. Sig. (2-sided)
Pearson Chi-Square	15.352	6	.018
Likelihood Ratio	15.843	6	.015
Linear-by-Linear Association	.450	1	.502
N of Valid Cases	928		

· 1 cells (8.3%) have expected count less than 5. The minimum expected c is .70.

The form of a 3 x 3 table with nominal variables is calculated by selecting a reference category (For ease, I will select Republican) for the columns and a reference category (favor) for the rows. We find that 35.4% of Republicans and 28.2% of Democrats favor increased taxes to build more prisons. The form of the relationship is Republicans are more likely than Democrats to favor the taxes. The extent of the relationship is estimated by subtracting the difference as 35.4 - 28.2 = 7.2%. Additional estimates can be made by selecting pairs of categories (e.g. Republican vs. Independent; and so on).

How much do we learn about opinions on this tax by knowing a person's political orientation? The Cramer's V statistic is appropriate for a 3 x 3 table. It's value is Cramer's V=.091, p<.05. The precision of the table is estimated by squaring the value (.091 x .091 = .008). Multiplying this number by 100 to get a percentage we obtain 0.8% or about 1%.

Symmetric Measures

		Value	Approx. Sig.
Nominal by Nominal	Phi	.129	.018
	Cramer's V	.091	.018
N of Valid Cases		928	·

Not assuming the null hypothesis.

Using the asymptotic standard error assuming the null hypothesi

We can only improve our estimate of a person's opinion about taxes to build more prisons by 1% if we know their political orientation. This is a very small number. Most social science research of bi-variate relationships will have low precision.

Summary interpretation

The 1995 National Opinion Survey of Crime and Justice asked Americans about their opinion on taxes (favor, oppose, and neutral) to build more prisons and their political preference

(Republican, Democrat, Independent, and Other). A chi-squared test can be used to determine if there is a statistical relationship between public opinion about taxes for building more prisons and political preference. We reject the null hypothesis (χ^2 (6) = 15.4, p<.05). We find that Republicans are about 7 percent more likely than Democrats and about 4 percent more likely than Independents to favor a tax to build more prisons. Note, however that only 35, 28, and 31 percent of Republicans, Democrats, and Independents would support this kind of tax. Few persons said they preferred another political preference making our estimates of their opinion unreliable. While there is a statistically significant difference in opinion about taxes for more prisons based on political preference, the results of this study should be viewed with caution since we can only explain about 1 percent of the variation in opinion about the proposed tax when we know a person's political preference.

A good summary of a cross-tabulation will note:

- the source of information
- how the variables were measured
- the decision on chi-square
- the form and extent of the relationship if chi-square is significant, and
- the limitations/strength of the analysis based on the precision of the relationship.

KEY TERMS

Cell
Column percentage
Chi-square
Cramer's V
Cross-tab
Low expected cell frequency
Non-parametric
Percentage down and compare across
Proportion reduction in error
Row percentage
Yate's correction

Web-sites

The *Sourcebook of Criminal Justice Statistics* Online: http://www.albany.edu/sourcebook/
    The Sourcebook provides a compilation of about 600 tables on characteristics of the US criminal justice system, public opinion, crime victimization and arrests, the courts, and corrections. It is an excellent referencing tool with summary tables and documentation about the original sources. For first time users, note that most of these tables report valid percentages and the independent variables will sometimes be presented in rows rather than columns.

Name _____   Date _____

Research Problems: Use the General Social Survey to calculate a chi-squared statistic to test the following hypothesis: Attitudes toward the death penalty (Cappun) in American vary by sex (Sex).

Use the codebook to identify the characteristics of variables.

Write out your hypothesis:

How big will the cross-tab be: (r x c = cells) _____ x _____ = _____

Draw the cross-tab with N's and column percentages:

Statistics(Chi-square and Phi or Cramer's V)

Calculate the precision (if appropriate)

Write a summary interpretation

Name _____   **Date** _____

Research Problems: Use the National Opinion Survey of Crime and Justice to calculate a chi-squared statistic to test the following hypothesis: Attitudes about crime rates (N9) will differ for persons who watch ACrime TV@ shows (M3).

Use the codebook to identify the characteristics of variables.

Write out your hypothesis:

How big will the cross-tab be: (r x c = cells) _____ x _____ = _____

Draw the cross-tab with N's and column percentages:

Statistics(Chi-square and Phi or Cramer's V)

Calculate the precision (if appropriate)

Write a summary interpretation

Name _____   **Date** _____

Research Problems: Use the Monitoring the Future Study to calculate a chi-squared statistic to test the following hypothesis: Marijuana use (V117) in the past 30 days will differ by sex (V150).

Use the codebook to identify the characteristics of variables.

Write out your hypothesis:

How big will the cross-tab be: (r x c = cells) _____ x _____ = _____

Draw the cross-tab with N's and column percentages:

Statistics(Chi-square and Phi or Cramer's V)

Calculate the precision (if appropriate)

Write a summary interpretation

Name _____   **Date** _____

Research Problems: Use the General Social Survey to calculate a chi-squared statistic to test the following hypothesis: Attitudes toward the abortion for any reason (Abany) in American vary by age (Age).

Use the codebook to identify the characteristics of variables.

Write out your hypothesis:

How big will the crosstab be: (r x c = cells) _____ x _____ = _____

(Remember that age goes from 18 through 89)

Use SPSS to calculate chi-squared.

What is the percentage of cells will low expected frequency counts? _____

Is this an acceptable percentage? Yes / No Explain.

Is this table easy to read? Yes / No

What could be done to improve it?   Explain.

Name _____   **Date** _____

Using methods that you learned in chapter 3, recode age into 3 or 4 age groups (e.g. 18 to 29; 30 to 54; 55 to 89). Recalculate chi-squared using the recoded variable.

Write out your hypothesis?

How big will the new cross-tab be: _____ x _____ = _____

Draw the new cross-tab with N's and column percentages

Statistics(Chi-square and Phi or Cramer's V)

Calculate the precision (if appropriate)

Write a summary interpretation

Name _____   **Date** _____

Research Problem:

Choose two variables from any of the data sets.

Use the codebook to identify the characteristics of all variables.

Write out your hypothesis:

How big will the cross-tab be: (r x c = cells) _____ x _____ = _____

Draw the cross-tab with N's and column percentages:

Statistics(Chi-square and Phi or Cramer's V)

Calculate the precision (if appropriate)

Write a summary interpretation

Name _____ **Date** _____

Research Problem:

Use Content Select to find two articles on police use of force.

Use the General Social Survey to calculate chi-squared statistics to test hypotheses for each of the police use of violence variables (Polabuse, polattak, polescap, polhitok, polmurdr) cross-tabulated by several variables of your choice.

What kinds of variables do you think will be related to public opinion about police use of force?

Write out one of your hypotheses here

Draw the cross-tab

Statistics

Continue on with additional tests. Write a four to six page paper summarizing the results of your research.

Name _____   Date _____

Use Fox's Statistics Calculator to calculate a two-way chi-square test.

Research Problem:

Is there a relationship between handedness and beer-drinking preference? A random sample of 35 right-handed and 35 left-handed people is drawn, and their preference for one of two major beer brands is recorded:

Beer	Handedness Right	Left
Schmoltz	25	18
Blatz	10	17

    a.   What is the null hypothesis

    b.   What is the alternative

    c.   What are the degrees of freedom? _____

    d.   Assuming an alpha of .05, what is the critical value of chi-square? _____

    e.   Assuming an alpha of .01, what is the critical value of chi-square? _____

    f.   What is the chi-square? _____

    g.   What is the statistical conclusion for both levels of alpha?

CORRELATION

INTRODUCTION

Correlation is introduced as a powerful technique for analyzing the linear relationship between two variables that are measured at the *interval* or *ratio* levels, and in a special case with two category nominal level variables. In this chapter, you will be introduced to correlation and its most popular version: Pearson's correlation (r). You will see that correlation tests the degree of association of variables allowing an interpretation of the form, extent and precision of bi-variate relationships.

SCATTERPLOTS

In a cross-tabulation the variables need to be discrete so that we can fit them into a cell within the table. Correlational analysis is a more powerful procedure because unlike cross-tabs we can work with variables with many categories and with continuous metrics. A scatterplot allows us to examine the joint distribution and a correlation allows us to describe the relationship between the variables.

A scatterplot is a plot of the position of each observation with the independent variable on the horizontal axis and the dependent variable on the vertical axis. The closer that the cases bunch together like a thin line, the stronger the association. Using a scatterplot, we may obtain a graphical presentation of the form, extent, and precision of relationships of variables measured at the interval and ratio level.

FORM OF RELATIONSHIPS IN SCATTERPLOTS

Let's look at some hypothetical data to illustrate different forms of relationships. Figure 1 shows a linear and a curvilinear relationship between seriousness of offense and length of sentence. Note that each point on the scatterplot represents a single person's score on each variable. A linear relationship will look like a straight line. A curvilinear relationship may take on many different forms. A scatterplot allows a quick check on the form. Note that most correlation coefficients assume that there is a linear relationship between variables. A scatterplot simply allows a visual test of the form of the relationship. In this chapter, we will take the conventional assumption that all of the relationships are linear.

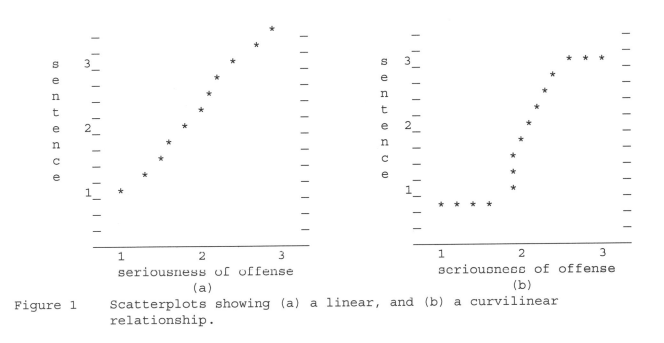

Figure 1   Scatterplots showing (a) a linear, and (b) a curvilinear relationship.

EXTENT OF RELATIONSHIPS IN SCATTERPLOTS

Moving to Figure 2, there are three scatterplots hypothetically illustrating the extent of association between the length of a prison sentence in relation to seriousness of offense. The extent of a correlation is positive if the joint values on the dependent variable increase as values on the independent variable increase. A negative correlation suggests that values on the independent variable increase the joint values on the dependent variable decrease. If there is no correlation between the variables the scores will appear to be randomly distributed throughout the scatterplot.

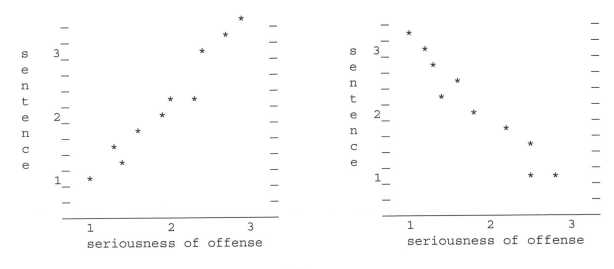

161

(a)   (b)

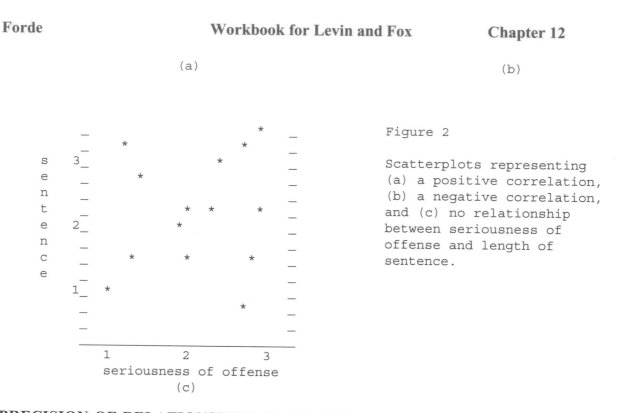

Figure 2

Scatterplots representing
(a) a positive correlation,
(b) a negative correlation,
and (c) no relationship
between seriousness of
offense and length of
sentence.

(c)

PRECISION OF RELATIONSHIPS IN SCATTERPLOTS

Scatterplots allow a visual estimation of the strength of association or the precision of relationships.   Figure 3 shows a strong and a weak relationship between sentence length and crime seriousness.   The strength of correlation is not dependent on its form or extent.   The strength refers to how closely the cases cluster along the line (in a linear relationship) or the curve (in a curvilinear relationship).

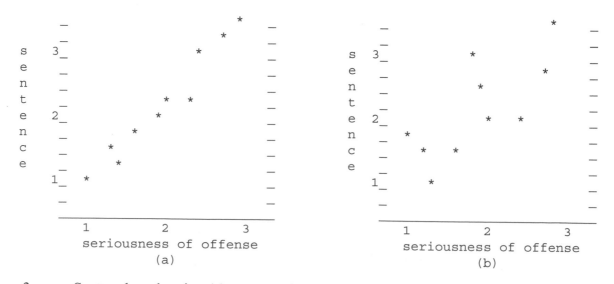

Figure 3   Scatterplots showing (a) a strong (linear) correlation and (b) a weak (linear)

correlation

PEARSON'S CORRELATION COEFFICIENT: *r*

Scatterplots provide a visual aid. We turn now to the numerical calculation of Pearson's correlation coefficient. With it we may determine the extent and precision of relationship between variables. The form is assumed to be linear. The formula for Pearson's correlation is:

$$= \frac{\Sigma(X - \overline{X})(Y - \overline{Y})}{\sqrt{\Sigma(X - \overline{X})^2 \Sigma(Y - \overline{Y})^2}}$$

The numerator is called the covariance of Y and X, where X and Y are the joint values on a variable for a case in comparison to the means of X and Y. The denominator is similar to a standard deviation of each variable. Thus, r is defined as the ratio of the product of the standard deviations of Y and X to the covariance of Y and X.

Form

The form of the relationship of Pearson's *r* refers to the direction of a correlation which may be positive (direct), negative (inverse), or null (zero).

Extent

The extent of *r* refers to the magnitude of the correlation. The extent ranges in magnitude from -1 to +1. For Pearson=s *r* we use a benchmark for the extent of the relationship: 0 to .2 is very weak; .2 to .4 is weak to moderate; .4 to .6 is moderate to strong; .6 to .8 is very strong; and .8 to 1 is very strong to perfect. Zero indicates no relationship between the variables. The further that *r* is from zero, the stronger the relationship.

Precision

The precision of a correlation may be estimated based on the magnitude of *r*. Simply, square it: r^2. The r-squared is a PRE statistic which we multiply by 100 to obtain the percentage reduction in error. Some textbooks call this a coefficient of determination or how much we can account for in the relationship between variables. Also, $1 - r^2$ is called the coefficient of non-determination or that which is unaccounted for in a relationship between variables.

Level of significance

The level of significance of *r* is calculated by converting it to a t score. The formula is:

$$= r \sqrt{\frac{N-2}{1-r^2}}$$

Where r = the calculated correlation coefficient; and N = the sample size.

Since we are using a t-test to test whether or not there is a significant relationship between variables you might guess that we're back to one and two-tailed tests of significance. You'd be right! We must specify a one or two tailed hypothesis before proceeding to our statistical analysis. SPSS prints the estimated level of significance for two-tailed tests as the default option. Like the t-test in Chapter 9, we simply divide the printed significance by two to obtain an estimate for a one-tailed significance.

DATA ANALYSIS EXAMPLE

Research Problem: Using the National Opinion Survey on Crime and Justice, what are the statistical relationships between opinions about policy on the legality of marijuana use (S1) and attitudes toward the legalization of selling of marijuana if it where legal to use (S2) correlated with peoples= age (D1) and sex (D16)?

Codebook information: Use the codebook to get basic information about each variable.

Opinions about marijuana policy on legalization of its use is a Likert scale ranging from entirely legal (1) to it should be a crime (4). We will assume that this is an interval level variable with a continuous metric of 1 unit of legal use.

Opinions about whether or not it should be legal to sell marijuana, if it were legal to use it, is a two category nominal level variable measured as yes (1) or no (2).

Age is measured at a continuous interval level as age in years (1 year intervals).

Sex of the respondent is a two category nominal level variable measured as male (1) or female (2).
Hypotheses:

Write out a research, null and alternative hypothesis for the research problems. You must specify hypotheses for each pairs of variables that you wish to test.

Research Hypothesis 1: Opinions about the legalization of marijuana use are such that older persons are less likely than younger persons to approve of it.	$\alpha = .05$
Null Hypothesis: Opinions about legalization of marijuana use are not correlated with a person=s age.	$H_0: r = 0$
Alternative Hypothesis: Opinions about legalization of marijuana use are such that Older persons are less likely than younger persons to approve of it.	$H_1: r > 0$ (one-tailed test)

Research Hypothesis 2: Males and females have the same opinion about public policy on the legalization of the use of marijuana.	$\alpha = .05$
Null Hypothesis: Males and females have the same opinion about public policy on the legalization of the use of marijuana.	$H_0: r - 0$
Alternative Hypothesis: Males and females have different opinions about public policy on legalization of the use of marijuana.	$H_1: r \neq 0$ (two-tailed test)

Research Hypothesis 3:	$\alpha = .05$
People who favor a policy legalizing the use of marijuana will say that it should be legal to sell marijuana if it is legal to use it.	
Null Hypothesis:	$H_0: r = 0$
Attitudes toward the legalization of selling of marijuana are independent of opinion about the legalization of the use of it.	
Alternative Hypothesis:	$H_1: r > 0$
People who favor a policy legalizing the use of marijuana will say that it should be legal to sell marijuana if it is legal to use it.	
	(one-tailed test)

Note that you may develop as many hypotheses as there are pairs of variables. You do not have to have a hypothesis for every pair. Hypotheses are only necessary for pairs where you wish to test a relationship. Here we will only examine three pairs.

Note that hypotheses 1 and 3 specify one-tailed tests. Why? Like we did with t-tests, we're specifying a direction for these correlations. We need to look at how the variables are measured to make our guess about the sign of the correlation coefficient (positive > 0; or negative < 0; or unknown $\neq 0$). I like to draw a picture with the dependent variable on the y axis and the independent variable on the x axis. Below are my hand-written scribbles for my guesses.

In hypothesis 1, I suspect that older people are more likely to disapprove of marijuana use. I've guessed that older people on average will disapprove and younger people will approve. Join the dots and it looks like a positive slope. Thus my alternative hypothesis is r >0.

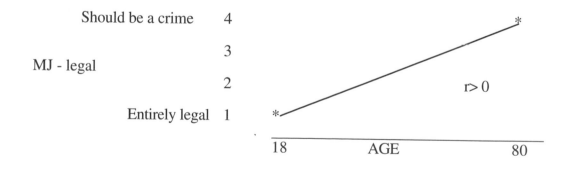

Hypothesis 2 uses an interval level dependent variable and a dichotomous level independent variable. It is useful to draw out a picture here to figure out the direction on the correlation.

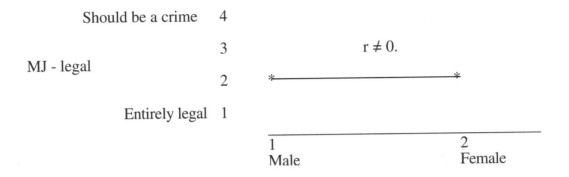

In this instance, I have no reason to expect that males and females would differ in opinions about policy on the legality of marijuana use. In fact, I suspect they both may say that it should be available for prescription use (about 2). Draw a dot at 2 on the MJ policy scale for males and another at 2 for females. Then, join the dots. While there are no possible values between male and female we can use the graph to help us to identify the direction of the correlation. In this case, the line is flat. Since we are not guessing a positive or a negative, we would write the alternative hypothesis as $r \neq 0$.

For hypothesis 3, draw "legal to sell" on the y-axis and legal to use on the x-axis. I expect that someone who supports a policy of legalization of marijuana for use will be more likely to say yes to the legalization to sell it. I'll draw a dot close to yes on the scale. For those persons who are in favor of a policy of criminalization of marijuana for use, I'm guessing they will still say no to legalization of selling marijuana even if it was legal to use it. Join the dots. We have a positive slope and thus our guess for the alternative hypothesis is $r > 0$.

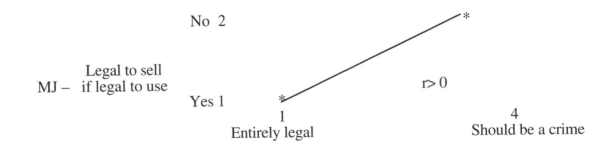

There are several ways to obtain correlations in SPSS. We will use the correlations procedure to obtain a *correlation matrix* requesting information on the correlation, the sample size, and the probability value based on a two-tailed level of significance. The procedure is obtained though ANALYZE, CORRELATE, and BIVARIATE. The dialogue box is shown below:

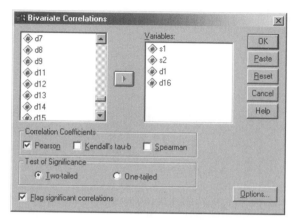

All of the variables are entered (in any order) into the same analysis. We select the Pearson correlation and two-tailed tests of significance. SPSS, by default, will "flag" correlations that are significant at the .01 level. It also prints the significance level. SPSS reports N's for each correlation as the number of cases where both elements are valid (e.g. a person answers both questions on a survey).

Computer output:

Correlations

		S1 WHICH S2 MARIJUANA POLICY TO YOU FAVOR	LEGAL TO SELL MARIJUANA IF LEGAL TO USE	D1 RESPONDANT'S AGE	D16 SEX OF RESPONDANT
S1 WHICH MARIJUANA POLICY DO YOU FAVOR	Pearson Correlation	1	.132**	-.042	-.037
	Sig. (2-tailed)	.	.000	.188	.243
	N	983	947	973	983
S2 LEGAL TO SELL MARIJUANA IF LEGAL TO USE	Pearson Correlation	.132**	1	.148**	.120**
	Sig. (2 tailed)	.000	.	.000	.000
	N	947	962	952	962
D1 RESPONDANTS AGE	Pearson Correlation	-.042	.148**	1	.102**
	Sig. (2-tailed)	.188	.000	.	.001
	N	973	952	994	994
D16 SEX OF RESPONDANT	Pearson Correlation	-.037	.120**	.102**	1
	Sig. (2 tailed)	.037	.000	.001	.
	N	983	962	994	1005

** Correlation is significant at the 0.01 level (2-tailed).

Let's look at the correlation matrix. Note the "1" for the correlation of S1 with S1, S2 with S2, and so on. These 1's allow an easy identification of the diagonal of the matrix. The significance of these correlations is printed as a dot which means it is not applicable. The N's here tell us the number of people who answered this particular question. So, 983 people gave us a valid answer about their opinion on policy about the legalization of marijuana use. How many people told us their age? And, their sex?

The correlations on either side of the diagonal (identity matrix) are symmetrical. Look at the correlation of S1 with S2 in column 1 and row 2 (r=.132). It is the same value as the correlation of S2 with S1 (r=.033) in column 2 and row 1. We can locate the correlation of two variables on either side of the diagonal. The APA manual recommends that only the top half of the correlation matrix be presented in a summary table.

If a one-tailed level of significance is required, it may be obtained from the printout by dividing the two-tailed probability value by two. While the one-tailed significance can be requested from SPSS (look back at the dialogue box), it is best to just ask for two tailed unless all hypotheses will be one-tailed. The general form for expressing a correlation is shown below:

General form: r = value, p-level (p<.05, or p>.05).

Interpretation of correlation coefficients:

The computer will print out r and a two-tailed probability for estimating its significance. We will use an alpha level of α = .05 to test the hypotheses.

Testing hypothesis 1, we find a negative correlation between attitudes toward the legalization of marijuana use and the age of respondents. Since we had expected a positive value for r we would fail to reject the null hypothesis based on r=-.04, p>.05. Find the value of -.042 in the matrix. Since we fail to reject the null hypothesis we do not calculate form, extent, nor precision.

Testing hypothesis 2, we find a negative correlation between attitudes toward the legalization of marijuana for use and the sex of the respondents. We used a two tailed test and thus read the significance directly from the computer output as r = -.04, p>.05. Find the values of r= -.037 and sig = .243 in the matrix. The significant is greater than .05 which means that we fail to reject the null hypothesis.

Testing hypothesis 3, we find a positive relationship between opinions about selling if legal and opinion about policy on marijuana use. Find r=.132 in the computer output. We had expected a positive correlation in our one-tailed hypothesis. Is .132 significant? We look at the computer output to find a two-tailed significance of .000. Divide .000 by 2 which obviously also yields .000. Always, in an exercise, do this division to show that you correctly understand that a one-tailed significance is obtained by dividing the two-tailed significance by two.

The computation of the correlation allows a numerical summary indicating the weak correlation. The actual scatterplot of S2 by S1 is shown below. Quite clearly the distribution of scores doesn't look much like an positive relationship. Unlike, the idealized plots shown at the beginning of this chapter it is often difficult to see graphically whether there is a relationship between variables with only a few categories.

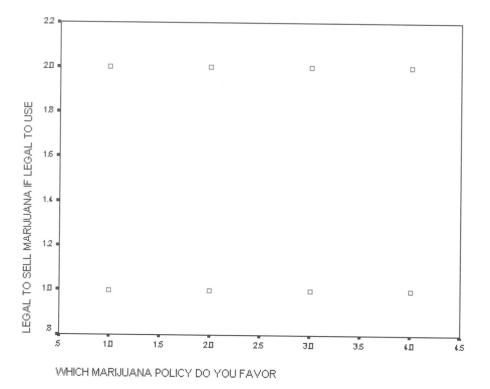

WHICH MARIJUANA POLICY DO YOU FAVOR

Testing hypothesis 3, we reject the null hypothesis based on $r=.13$, $p<.05$. (Find the value of Pearson's r in the table as .132, and calculate the one-tailed probability as .000 divided by 2). When the null hypothesis is rejected, we calculate form, extent, and precision. The form is positive. The extent is very weak. We have a significant positive correlation between opinions that it should be legal to sell marijuana if it is legal to use it and opinions about public policy on the use of marijuana. The precision of this relationship is very low ($r^2=.0169$ or 1.7%).

Summary Interpretation

The 1995 National Opinion Survey of Crime and Justice queried Americans about their opinions on governmental policy on the use of marijuana, and whether or not they felt it should be legal to sell marijuana if it were legal to use marijuana. The question on public policy was measuring using a four point scale ranging from entirely legal (1) to it should be a crime (4). The question on legalization of selling marijuana if it were legal to use was a yes (1) or no (2) question. A correlational analysis was used to determine whether age and sex are related to opinions about governmental policy, and whether there is a relationship between attitudes about use of marijuana and opinion about legalization of selling it. The correlations between age and sex with opinions about policy on the use of marijuana were not significant (p>.05). Opinion about selling it was significantly related to opinion about policies on the use of it (r=.13, p<.05). However, the significance of this relationship must be considered with great caution. It is a very weak statistical relationship that explains only 1.7% of the variation in opinion about selling of marijuana.

When writing up a correlational analysis:

- State the source of information
- Describe the measurement of each of the variables.
- Indicate the level of confidence
- State the decision on the null hypothesis as reject or fail to reject
- If significance, calculate form, extent, and precision
- Use a table if there are a large number of variables in an analysis. APA format suggests reporting the top half of the matrix.
- If only a few correlation statistics are reported they can be done in the text of a summary.

Key words

Correlation
Correlation matrix
Pearson's *r* (note the italics)
Diagonal of matrix
Inverse (negative)
Direct (positive)
Linear correlation
Scatterplot

Name _____   **Date** _____

1.   Research Problems: Use the National Opinion Survey of Crime and Justice to calculate Pearson's *r* to test the following hypotheses:

Research hypothesis 1.   Females are more likely than males (D16) to worry about getting mugged (W3).

Research hypothesis 2.   There is a correlation between worrying about getting mugged (W3) and a respondent=s age (D1).

Research hypothesis 3.   Females are more likely than males (D16) to worry about getting murdered (W5).

Research hypothesis 4.   Add a pair of variables of your own selection. You may pair one of the above variables with one additional variable.

Use the codebook to identify the characteristics of variables.

Write out the null and alternative hypotheses (draw diagrams to identify the direction for one-tailed hypotheses)

Name _____   **Date** _____

Record the correlation matrix for these variables (Pearson's *r*).

Interpret the results

2.   *Research Problems:* Use the Monitoring the Future Study to calculate Pearson's *r* to test the following hypotheses:

Research hypothesis 1.   Year of study (year) and reported use of cocaine (V124).
Research hypothesis 2.   Students who approve of cheating (V1687) are more likely to get speeding tickets V197).
Research hypothesis 3.   Opinion about the risk of cocaine (v1795) is directly related to reported use of cocaine (124)
Research hypothesis 4.   Add a pair of variables of your own selection. You may pair one of the above variables with one additional variable.

Use the codebook to identify the characteristics of variables.

Write out the null and alternative hypotheses (draw diagrams to identify the direction for one-tailed hypotheses)

Name _____   **Date** _____

Record the correlation matrix for these variables (Pearson's *r*).

Interpret the results

Name _____   **Date** _____

3.   *Research Problems:* Use the General Social Survey to calculate Pearson's *r* to test hypotheses about relationships between questions on abortion, sex of the respondent, age, and political views.

Write out your hypotheses:

Use the codebook to identify the characteristics of variables.

Name _____   **Date** _____

Record the correlation matrix for these variables (Pearson's *r)*.

Interpret the results

Name _____   **Date** _____

4.   Use Content Select to find two articles on the relationship between parent's and children's educational attainment.

Identify two or more variables in the Monitoring the Future Study that would allow a test of this relationship.

Identify two or more variables in the General Social Study that would allow a test of this relationship.

Name _____   **Date** _____

5.   Use Fox's Statistics Calculator to calculate Pearson's *r*.

A researcher was interested in determining the degree of association between IQ (X) and years of employment (Y). She recruited 9 subjects, each of whom took an IQ test and reported the number of years they have been continuously employed. The results were:

Subject	IQ	Years Employed
A	115	6
B	125	5
C	109	4
D	132	3
E	116	8
F	141	2
G	153	1
H	122	2
I	120	7

a.   What is Pearson's r? _____

b.   What is the critical value of r, assuming a value of .01? _____

c.   Is the correlation between IQ and years employed significant at the .01 level?

d.   If appropriate, interpret the form, extent, and precision.

Name _____   **Date** _____

Based on your readings of Levin and Fox on correlation and partial correlation:

6.   Consider the following correlation matrix for age (X), credit card debt (Y), and salary (Z) for a random sample of 50 people between the ages of 18 and 40.

	Age	Debt	Salary
Age	1.00	0.30	0.55
Debt	0.30	1.00	-0.20
Salary	0.55	-0.20	1.00

a.   Which correlation(s) is / are significant at the .05 level of significance?

b.   Which correlation(s) is / are significant at the .05 level of significance?

c.   What is the partial correlation between age and debt, holding salary constant?

d.   Is the partial correlation smaller, equal to or greater than the simple correlation between age and debt?

Name _____   **Date** _____

7.   Use the Monitoring the Future Study to calculate Pearson's *r* to test whether boys are more likely than girls (V150) to report use of cocaine (V124).

     a.   Record and interpret the results

     b.   What other statistical procedure(s) could you use to test this hypothesis?

     c.   Which procedure do you feel provides the best information. Explain your choice.

REGRESSION ANALYSIS

INTRODUCTION

Regression analysis is one of the most powerful methods for analyzing linear relationships between two variables measured at the interval or ratio levels. Essentially, regression analysis may be used to identify an **association** between variables and to use this information to make **predictions** about the value of a dependent variable from one or more independent variables.

Correlation analysis is used to inform us about the accuracy of predictions from regression and to describe the nature of the relationship. This chapter introduces you to regression analysis by having you work with examples using two and then three variables that are assumed to be linearly related to each other. We will interpret the form, extent and precision of these relationships.

REGRESSION MODEL

Let's begin with some hypothetical data on sentencing and the seriousness of the crime. Sentence length is operationalized as time in years. Seriousness of the crime is a scale going from not at all serious (0) to extremely serious (10). A researcher examines ten cases selected at random from her local court:

Case	Sentence	Seriousness of crime
1	12	3
2	20	10
3	25	10
4	3	1
5	4	1
6	3	2
7	15	7
8	18	6
9	1	1
10	2	2

Regression analysis allows us to see whether or not there is a relationship between the length of a sentence and the seriousness of a crime. A scatterplot is shown on the next page.

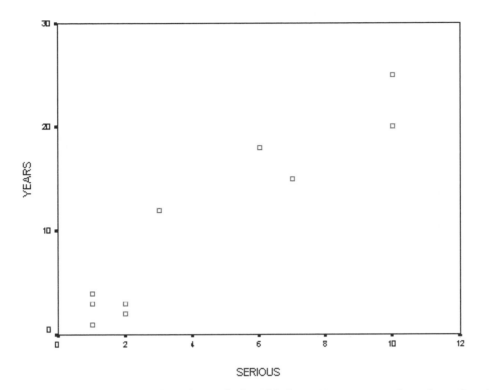

It appears to the eye that there is a relationship between sentence length and seriousness of the offense. Regression analysis assumes that there is a linear relationship between variables. Where would we draw a straight line on the above scatterplot? Regression analysis will tell us where to draw the line so that we can minimize the errors in our estimate for a predicted value.

Levin and Fox, in Chapter 11, provide a discussion of the foundations of regression. The formula for the regression line is shown below:

$$y = a + b\,x + e$$

The relationship between variables is assumed to be linear approximated by a straight line with a slope (b) and an intercept (a). The slope of a line is defined as the vertical distance divided by the horizontal distance between any two points on the regression line. The intercept is the point where the regression line intersects with the y-axis (where x = zero). We use the term Ae@ to represent the residual (or error) in predicting y from x.

The regression line is drawn on to the figure on the next page using the coordinates (x, y) for the intercept (0, .50) and the means of x and y (4.3, 10.3).

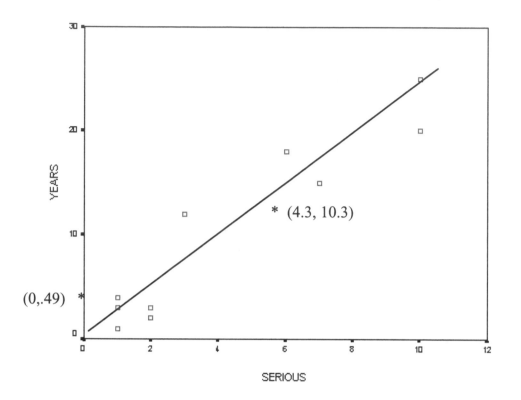

* (4.3, 10.3)

(0,.49) *

Notice that some of the scores fall below the line while others are above it. The regression line is the best guess for the relationship between the variables. The regression procedure will tell how well we are able to do in our estimates. Have a look back at Levin and Fox's chapter to see how the intercept and slope are calculated. Here in the workbook, we're going to look at the computer output and go beyond it to show how regression analysis can be used to make predictions.

In regression analysis, a mathematical equation is used to predict the value of the dependent variable ($\hat{y}$) for a given a value of the independent variable (x).

$$\hat{y} = a + b\,x$$

When we find a significant relationship between variables, we can use the regression line to predict values of the dependent variable for expressed values of an independent variable. A regression analysis of seriousness on sentencing yields an intercept of .48 and a slope of 2.28. The table on the next page shows the expected (predicted) sentence length for crimes with seriousness of 1, 5, and 8. Using a regression equation, we predict that people who commit crimes of serious "1" are expected to get a sentence of 2.77 years in prison.

184

$\hat{y} = a + b\,x$ predicting sentence length based on crime seriousness			
$\hat{y}$	a	b	X
2.77	0.49	2.28	1
11.89	0.49	2.28	5
18.73	0.49	2.28	8

The regression line for $\hat{y}$ is a best guess for a predicted value. Most cases in a regression analysis will fall above or below the regression line. The difference between the best guess and the actual value for a case is called a residual (or error) in predicting y from x. For these hypothetical data, regression analysis provides a PRE statistic (r-squared) suggesting that there is a very strong relationship between these variables so that we will be correct 89 percent of the time. Let's go to the computer output using some real data to illustrate the steps to interpret a regression model.

Form

In regression we will assume that relationships between variables are linear. There are other types of non-linear regression models but they fall outside the scope of an introductory course.

Extent

In regression, we may examine two aspects of the extent of relationships: unstandardized and standardized. The extent of relationships refers to the slope of a regression line. The slope is conceptualized as the number of units that the y variable will increase given a value of x. The unstandardized slope (beta or b) use the original metrics of y and x. The standardized slope (BETA or B) is identical to correlation in bivariate regression where the standard deviations of both variables are used to estimate the slope of the regression line.

The magnitude of the extent of the slope of an unstandardized regression line will depend on the attributes of the variables that are being examined (e.g. dollars, crimes, behaviors, etc.). The extent of BETA ranges from -1 to +1, and the extent refers to whether the sign is positive (direct) or negative (inverse) and its magnitude.

Level of significance of the slope

In regression, a researcher will want to know whether the statistical significance of a slope is large enough to reject the null hypothesis that a slope is zero. Recall that the extent of a slope may be positive, negative, or zero. A researcher may also use a one or two-tailed test of their hypothesis.

A t-test is used to evaluate the significance of a slope. Recall that a t-test compared individual scores to a population mean, and a standard deviation. A regression analysis calculates a t-test by comparing the position of individual scores to a regression line, and divided by the standard error of the slope. As in t-tests, we have to specify a one or two-tailed hypothesis for each independent variable.

Precision

The precision of a regression line is estimated by using a correlation coefficient. The coefficient of determination may be determined from the magnitude of r by squaring it. A larger value of r^2 indicates a stronger fit of scores around the regression line. In multiple regression we use an adjusted r^2 which is adjusted to take into account the number of independent variables in the equation.

DATA ANALYSIS EXAMPLE

Research Problem: Is marijuana and hashish use (v115) related to a person's perception about citizenry and obeying the law (v1672).

We will use regression analysis to examine this issue using a sample of High School Students from the 1990 and 2000 Monitoring the Future Study.

Codebook information: Use the codebook to get basic information about each variable.

The use of marijuana or hashish is measured using a "normalized scale" 1 "0 occassions" to 7 "40 or more times." We will treat this as if it were an interval level scale with a known metric of 1 unit of use.

Obeying the law to be a good citizen is measured by a statement where the students were read "I feel that you can't be a good citizen unless you always obey the law" and asked to rate their level of agreement with the statement on a scale of disagree (1) to agree (5).

Hypothesis: Write out a research, null and alternative hypothesis for the research problem. We will use a .05 level of significance.

Research Hypothesis:
    Marijuana and hashish use will be higher as students disagree
    with the statement that a good citizen must always obey the law.
	$\alpha = $ .05

Null Hypothesis:
    Marijuana and hashish use will be independent of attitudes about
    good citizenry and the law.
	$H_0: \beta = 0$

Alternative Hypothesis:
    Marijuana and hashish use is inversely related to attitudes about
    good citizenry (draw a picture like in correlation to see the direction)
 	
	$H_1: \beta < 0$
	
	(one-tailed test)

Note in regression that the notation in the hypothesis uses the standardized slope (Beta; _).

The regression procedure is accessed by clicking on ANALYZE, REGRESSION, and then LINEAR. The dialogue box follows:

Move the dependent variable and independent variables into their respective boxes. We will use the default method to "enter" the variables into the regression model. If you wish, you can also check "descriptives" in the "Statistics" box to get the means for the two variables.

Computer output:

A large amount of information is produced in the regression output with many features that you will not need for bi-variate regression. You will have to look in the output for the appropriate bi-variate regression statistics. Most programs provide a model summary, an ANOVA test, and the regression coefficients.

The regression table is the most relevant piece for bi-variate regression. The regression coefficients table provides unstandardized slopes, an intercept, standardized slopes, and t-values with their two-tailed significance. Regression procedures generate more information than is required leaving it up to the reader to extract the information that he or she needs.

Coefficients

Model		Unstandardized Coefficients		Standardized Coefficients		
		B	Std. Error	Beta	t	Sig.
1	(Constant)	3.737	.079		47.236	.000
	V1672 001A011A:-OBY					
	LW=-GD CTZ	-.389	.025	-.223	-15.567	.000

a. Dependent Variable: V115 022B07A:#XMJ+HS/LIFETIME

The ANOVA test tells us whether or not there is a relationship between the dependent variable and the predictor variable(s).

ANOVA

Model		Sum of Squares	df	Mean Square	F	Sig.
1	Regression	1149.373	1	1149.373	242.328	.000
	Residual	21974.488	4633	4.743		
	Total	23123.861	4634			

a. Predictors: (Constant), V1672 001A011A:-OBY LW=-GD CTZ

b. Dependent Variable: V115 002B07A:#XMJ+HS/LIFETIME

The ANOVA test gives the same information as a t-test and it provides the basis for calculation of the coefficient of determination (precision).

The model summary for our example is shown below. This information could also be calculated by hand using the ANOVA table.

```
              Model Summary
```

Nodel	R	Rsquare	Adjusted R Square	Std. Error of the Estimate
1	.223[a]	.050	.049	2.178

a. Predictors: (Constant), V1672 001A011A:-OBY LW=-GD CTZ

Interpretation

We will interpret the features of the regression line: form, extent and precision. We will also use the regression line to predicted value for a person who disagrees that a person must always obey the law to be a good citizen (1). Note that we will use an alpha level of _ = .05 to test our hypothesis.

The form of all regression lines is assumed to be linear. Keep this in mind as we make our interpretation.

In testing the hypothesis, we look to the t-value testing the slope for the independent variable. We had expected a negative value of _ < 0. It is negative and it has a t=-15.567. We reject the null hypothesis that the slope of Beta (_) is zero. We find that _ = -.23, p<.05. (Remember on a one-tailed test that the significance is based on t with its probability of .000 divided by 2 equal to .000).

The extent of the relationship provides the most useful information.   Using the same benchmark that we used for correlations, we say that we find a weak to moderate relationship between marijuana and hashish use and attitudes toward citizenry and the law. The standardized slope (_ = -.23) can be interpreted like a correlation coefficient telling us that this is a weak to moderate relationship.

Regression is a more powerful tool than correlation. When we reject the null hypothesis we can use the unstandardized values to make predictions about our dependent variable. Our predicted value (ŷ) can be estimated using information from the table.

$$\hat{y} = a + b\,x$$

a is the intercept or constant
b is the unstandardized slope; and
x is the value we wish to insert for the independent variable

In our example, we insert the information from the regression table to get
$\hat{y} = 3.737 + -.389\,(1)$

$\hat{y} = 3.348$ or 3

A 3 on the 1 to 7 scale corresponds with a predicted value of trying marijuana or hashish 3-5 times.

The precision of the relationship is weak ($r^2 = .050$; rounded as $r^2 = .05$). We find that we are able to explain about 5 percent of the variation in reported marijuana and hashish use based on attitudes about citizenry and the importance of obeying the law.

In bi-variate regression, we can also draw a regression line on a scatterplot. Look back at the codebook for the values for each variable. On the y-axis, draw out marijuana or hashish use on its 1 to 7 scale. On the x-axis, citizenry has 1 to 5 scale. Extend each of these scales past their ends so that they include a 0. Draw the intercept as (0, 3.7) and the means as (2.9, 2.6). Join the dots and you have a regression line predicting marijuana or hashish use based on attitudes about citizenry and the importance of obeying the law.

MULTIPLE REGRESSION

Multiple regression is interpreted in much the same way as bi-variate regression. We will illustrate the procedure by adding three additional variables to the bi-variate regression analysis. In adding three new variables, we need three additional hypotheses:

- We hypothesize that students who report drinking more alcohol (v104) will report more use of marijuana or hashish.
- We expect sex differences (v150) in use of marijuana or hashish
- We will test to see whether high school students in 2000 are different than high school students in 1990 (year of the study; v1).

Both sex and year are dichotomous nominal variables. A 2-N variable in regression is treated the same as a 2-N variable in correlation.

Our ultimate goal is to see which variables may help us to understand marijuana and hashish use among American High School Students.

Computer output in multiple regression.

In multiple regression we start with the ANOVA table. Similarly to the One-way ANOVA that we completed in Chapter 10, we need to check the F-ratio as an omnibus test. If the F-ratio is significant, then we will continue to read the output to look at the regression model. In this example, $F_{(4, 4192)} = 492.1$, $p < .05$. It is significant which means that it is appropriate to continue with the regression analysis. At least one of the variables is expected to explain some variation in the dependent variable.

ANOVA

Model		Sum of Squares	df	Mean Square	F	Sig.
1	Regression	6455.373	4	1613.843	492.110	.000
	Residual	13747.410	4192	3.279		
	Total	20202.784	4196			

a. Predictors: (Constant), V1 YEAR OF ADMIN (4-DIGITS), V150 002C03 :R'S SEX, V1672 001A011A:-OBY LW=-GD 002B04A:#X ALC/LIF SIPS

b. Dependent Variable: V115 002B07A:#XMJ+HS/LIFETIME

The t-tests are used to test the significance of the slopes for each of the independent variables. Recall that we stated a direction on obeying the law and on drinking so that these were one tailed tests. Thus, we need to divide the significance of their t-tests by two. The hypotheses for sex and year were non-directional two-tailed tests. We simply read their t-tests directly from the output.

Coefficients

Model		Unstandardized Coefficients		Standardized Coefficients		
		B	Std. Error	Beta	t	Sig.
1	(Constant)	-134.513	11.381		-11.819	.000
	V1672 001A011A:-OBY LW=-GD CTZ	-.161	.023	-.093	-7.129	.000
	V104 002B04A:#X ALC/LIF SIPS	.541	.013	.532	40.477	.000
	V150 002C03 :R'S SEX	-6.779E-02	.056	-.015	-1.207	.227
	V1 YEAR OF ADMIN (4-DIGITS)	6.777E-02	.006	.153	11.892	.000

a. Dependent Variable: V115 002B07A:#XMJ+HS/LIFETIME

Looking at the standardized betas and their t-tests we find that high school students reported use of marijuana or hashish has a:

- weak relation to attitudes toward obeying the law _ = -.09, p<.05
- moderate to strong relation with drinking _ = .53, p<.05
- no relation with sex of the student _= -.02, p>.05
- a weak relation with year of the study _=.15, p<.05
  (Note the positive coefficient suggests greater use of marijuana or hashish in higher years; 2000 is more than 1990)

The standardized betas can be used to indicate the relative importance of each variable. The magnitude of a standardized beta indicates its importance. In this example, self reported drinking of alcohol is the strongest predictor of marijuana or hashish use.

There are a variety of acceptable formats for presenting the results of a regression model. Most writers include the b, standard error, B and use asterisks to indicate significant variables. The computer output can be rounded to 2 or 3 significant figures. Since the dependent variable for this model was measured on a 1 to 7 scale, I would recommend 2 decimal places. The information, simply is not precise enough to allow more than 2.

Next, we can use the unstandardized betas to make a prediction about the dependent variable. We substitute each unstandardized slope into the prediction equation. Some statisticians suggest removing non-significant variables before doing this prediction. Others suggest simply leaving the variables in the equation because the computation is minimally influenced by their inclusion. We will leave sex of the respondent in our model.

Any values on each the scales may be used to make a prediction. Since there are many possibilities, you should pick values that are important for your research problem. For illustration, I will estimate a predicted value for students with the following attributes: disagree (1), drank 40 or more times (7), male (1), and 2000 (2000).

The prediction equation is: $\hat{y} = a + b_1 x_1 + b_2 x_2 + b_3 x_3 + b_4 x_4$

In our example, $\hat{y} = -134.513 + .161 (1) + .541 (7) + -.068 (1) + .068 (2000)$

$$\hat{y} = 5.045 = \text{about } 5$$

Go back to the codebook, for a 5, we predict that a student such as this will have tried marijuana or hashish about 10-19 times in their lifetime.

The model summary reports the precision of a multiple regression model. In multiple regression, use the adjusted $r^2 = .319$ or .32 which takes into account the number of variables in the model. This is often converted into a PRE statistic by multiplying it by 100 to obtain 32%. This is a relatively high amount for social science model.

Model Summary

Model	R	R Square	Adjusted R Square	Std. Error of the Estimate
1	.565	.320	.319	1.811

Predictors: (Constant), V1 YEAR OF ADMIN (4-DIGITS), V150 002C03 :F
V1672 001A011A:-OBY LW=-GD CTZ, V104 002B04A:#X ALC/LIF SIPS

We have covered a lot of ground with multiple regression. A summary interpretation of a regression model should report:

- source of information
- hypotheses for each independent variable
- a summary table of the regression coefficients
- whether variables were removed from the final model
- the adjusted r-squared
- some key predictions to answer the researchers most important issues

Key terms

Adjusted r-squared
Beta
Coefficient of determination
F-Ratio
Intercept
Linear regression
Model summary
Multiple regression
Predicted value
Slope
r-squared
Unstandardized beta

Research Problems: Use linear regression to test the following hypothesis:

From the GSS, there is a direct relationship between income (Rincom98) and education (degree).

Use the codebook to identify the characteristics of variables.

Write out the null and alternative hypotheses

Calculate the regression model

What is the predicted value of income for one category of education?

Interpret the results

Name _____   **Date** _____

Add another variable of interest to you to the model

What is your hypothesis?

Recalculate the regression model

Interpret the new results

Use Content Select to find two articles on income inequality. Write a short paper comparing the results of your analysis to research in these articles.

Name _____   **Date** _____

Research Problems: Use linear regression to test the following hypothesis:

From the MTF study, boys are more likely than girls (V150) to get speeding tickets V197.

Use the codebook to identify the characteristics of variables.

Write out the null and alternative hypotheses

Calculate the regression model

What is the predicted number of speeding tickets for:

Boys _____

Girls _____

Interpret the results

Name _____   **Date** _____

Add another variable of interest to you to the model

What is your hypothesis?

Recalculate the regression model

Interpret the new result

Use Content Select to find two articles on driving behavior. Compare your findings with their work.

Research Problems: Use linear regression to test a hypothesis:

Choose two variables from any data set.

Use the codebook to identify the characteristics of variables.

Write out the null and alternative hypotheses

Calculate the regression model

Make a prediction for one value of the independent variable:

Draw a scatterplot and draw the regression line using the intercept and means.

Name _____   **Date** _____

A complete regression analysis consists of a descriptive analysis of every variable in the regression model. Develop a regression model with four variables using any data set.

Describe the variables. Generate frequency distributions for each to obtain means and standard deviations. Assess skewness and kurtosis.

Frequencies

Dependent variable

Independent variable 1

Independent variable 2

Independent variable 3

Specify your hypotheses for regression.

Use linear regression to enter the independent variables. Summarize the results of your analysis.

Name _____   **Date** _____

Use Fox's Statistics Calculator to conduct a regression analysis of the following:

A research has gathered data from seven randomly selected employees on the number of years (X) employees have worked in a particular department and their salaries (Y) in thousands of dollars.

No. Years (X)	Salaries (Y)
1	18.5
2	20
2	20.25
4	21.5
5	25
7	26
7	27.5

a.   What is the slope of the regression line? _____

b.   What is the intercept of the regression line? _____

c.   Using the F-ratio, are these results significant at the .01 level?

d.   What would the predicted salary be for someone in the department who has worked 6 years? _____

e.   What is the prediction error for someone who has worked in the department for 6 years?

INSTRUCTIONAL CODEBOOK

SELECTED VARIABLES
FROM

MONITORING THE FUTURE:
A CONTINUING STUDY OF THE LIFESTYLES
AND VALUES OF YOUTH, 1990 and 2000

(ICPSR 9745 and 3184)

Principal Investigators

Lloyd D. Johnston, Jerald G. Bachman
and Patrick M. O'Malley

PREFACE

The following collection of data is a subset from the 1990 and 2000 releases of the longitudinal study of the lifestyles and values of youth in America. This codebook draws selected excerpts directly from the original study.

The data (and tabulations) utilized in this booklet were made available (in part) by the Inter-university Consortium for Political and Social Research (ICPSR). The data for MONITORING THE FUTURE: A CONTINUING STUDY OF THE LIFESTYLES AND VALUES OF YOUTH, Annual were originally collected by Lloyd D. Johnston, Jerald G. Bachman and Patrick M. O'Malley. Neither the collector of the original data nor the Consortium bears any responsibility for the analyses or interpretations presented here.

DATA COLLECTION DESCRIPTION

MONITORING THE FUTURE: A CONTINUING STUDY OF THE LIFESTYLES AND VALUES OF YOUTH, Annual, which is conducted by the University of Michigan's Institute for Social Research and receives its core funding from the National Institute on Drug Abuse, is an unusually comprehensive research project in several respects: surveys are conducted annually on an ongoing basis; the samples are large and nationally representative; and the subject matter is very broad, encompassing some 1300 variables per year.

The Monitoring the Future Project is designed to explore changes in many important values, behaviors, and lifestyle orientations of contemporary American youth. Two general types of tasks may be distinguished. The first is to provide a systematic and accurate description of the youth population of interest in a given year, and to quantify the direction and rate of the changes taking place among them over time. The second task, more analytic than descriptive, involves the explanation of the relationships and trends observed to exist.

INTRODUCTION

DATA COLLECTION PROCEDURES

The basic research design involves annual data collections from high school seniors during the spring of each year, beginning with the class of 1975. Each data collection takes place in approximately 125 public and private high schools selected to provide an accurate cross-section of high school seniors throughout the United States.

One limitation in the design is that it does not include in the target population those young men and women who drop out of high school before graduation (or before the last few months of the senior year, to be more precise). This excludes a relatively small proportion of each age cohort -- between 15 and 20 percent -- though not an unimportant segment, since certain behaviors, such as drug usage and delinquency tend to be higher than average in this group. For the purposes of estimating changes from one cohort of high school seniors to another, the omission of dropouts represents a problem only if different cohorts have considerably different proportions who drop out. There is no reason to expect dramatic changes in those rates for the foreseeable future, and recently published government statistics indicate a great deal of stability in dropout rates since 1970.

CONTENT AREAS AND QUESTIONNAIRE DESIGN

Drug use and related attitudes are the topics which receive the most extensive coverage in the Monitoring the Future project; but the questionnaires also deal with a wide range of other subject areas, including attitudes about government, social institutions, race relations, changing roles for women, educational aspirations, occupational aims, and marital and family plans, as well as a variety of background and demographic factors.

FILE STRUCTURE

The variables described in this codebook are a subset taken from the core and form 1 of MONITORING THE FUTURE: A CONTINUING STUDY OF THE LIFESTYLES AND VALUES OF YOUTH, 1990 and 2000. A full description of the original data structure, files, and representative publications can be obtained from the ICPSR data library.
The dataset is readable by the Statistical Package for the Social Sciences (SPSS © for Windows).

The instructional file is named:

  MTF90_00.sav

MISSING DATA

  The original data file contained several missing codes for non-response. People may refuse to answer some questions, they don't know, or a question may have been not applicable. These codes are collapsed into a single category in the instructional dataset (usually as –9).

CODEBOOK INFORMATION

  The codebook available for this study is not of the usual sort created by ICPSR. Rather, it is an edited version of the annual ISR volumes put into codebook form. It should also be noted that the codebook unlike the usual codebook is arranged by question numbers which do not coincide with the variable numbers. For user convenience, a sequential reference number has been added.

The example below is a reproduction of information appearing in the machine-readable codebook for a typical variable.

V139[1]   **#X**

'H'/LIFETIME [2]   **REF 37**[3]

On how many occasions (if any) have you used heroin   (smack, horse, skag)... in your lifetime?[4]

1[5]   0 occasions[6]
2   1-2
3   3-5
4   6-9
5   10-19
6   20-39
7   40 or more

```
° ° ° °1 Mneumonic name of variable.

° ° ° °2 Variable label.

° ° ° °3 Variable reference number.

° ° ° °4 Text from the questionnaire giving the wording for the question.

° ° ° °5 Values in the data for the variable.

° ° ° °6 Value label.
```

VARIABLE DESCRIPTION LIST: INSTRUCTIONAL DATASET

VAR NO.   **VARIABLE LABEL**   **REF NO.**

V13   **SCHL RGN-4 CAT**   **REF 1**

School region
   1. NORTHEAST: Maine, New Hampshire, Vermont,
      Massachusetts, Rhode Island, Connecticut, New York,
      New Jersey, and Pennsylvania
   2. NORTH CENTRAL: Ohio, Indiana, Illinois, Michigan,
      Wisconsin, Minnesota, Iowa, Missouri, North Dakota,
      South Dakota, Nebraska, and Kansas
   3. SOUTH: Delaware, Maryland, District of Columbia,
      Virginia, West Virginia, North Carolina, South
      Carolina, Georgia, Florida, Kentucky, Tennessee, Alabama
      Mississippi, Arkansas, Louisiana, Oklahoma, and
      Texas
   4. WEST: Montana, Idaho, Wyoming, Colorado, New Mexico,
      Arizona, Utah, Nevada, Washington, Oregon, and
      California

V150   **902C03 :R'S SEX**   **REF 2**
       MISSING -9

   C03: What is your sex?
      1. Male
      2. Female

V151   **902C04 :R'S RACE**   **REF 3**
       MISSING -9

   C04: How do you describe yourself?
      0. White or Caucasian
      1. Black or Afro-American
   NOTE: American Indian, Mexican American or Chicano,
      Puerto Rican or other Latin American, Oriental
      or Asian American, and Other were recoded to
      missing by the PI for reasons of confidentiality.

V49   # SIBLINGS   REF 4
MISSING -9

C07ab: How many brothers and sisters do you have? (Include step brothers and sisters and half-brothers and sisters.)
0. None
1. One
2. Two
3. Three or more

V163   902C08 :FATHR EDUC LEVEL   REF 5
MISSING -9

C08: What is the highest level of schooling your father completed?
1. Completed grade school or less
2. Some high school
3. Completed high school
4. Some college
5. Completed college
6. Graduate or professional school after college

V164   902C09 :MOTHR EDUC LEVEL   REF 6
MISSING -9

C09: What is the highest level of schooling your mother completed?
1. Completed grade school or less
2. Some high school
3. Completed high school
4. Some college
5. Completed college
6. Graduate or professional school after college

V166   902C11 :R'S POLTL PRFNC   REF 7
MISSING -9
C11: How would you describe your political preference?
1. Strongly Republican
2. Mildly Republican
3. Mildly Democrat
4. Strongly Democrat
5. Independent Party or No Preference
7. Other

V167   **902C12 :R'POL BLF RADCL**   **REF 8**
              MISSING -9

C12: How would you describe your political beliefs?
1. Very conservative
2. Conservative
3. Moderate
4. Liberal
5. Very liberal
6. Radical

V172   **902C15 :R'S HS PROGRAM**   **REF 9**
              MISSING -9

C15: Which of the following best describes your present high school program?
1. Academic or college prep
2. General
3. Vocational, technical, or commercial
4. Other, or don't know

V173   **902C16 :RT SF SCH AB>AVG**   **REF 10**
              MISSING -9

C16: Compared with others your age throughout the country, how do you rate yourself on school ability?
1. Far below average
2. Below average
3. Slightly below average
4. Average
5. Slightly above average
6. Above average
7. Far above average

V174   **902C17 :RT SF INTELL>AVG**   **REF 11**
              MISSING -9

C17: How intelligent do you think you are compared with others your age?
1. Far below average
2. Below average
3. Slightly below average
4. Average
5. Slightly above average
6. Above average
7. Far above average

V176   **902C18B:#DA/4W SC MS CUT**   **REF 12**
         MISSING -9

       C18: During the LAST FOUR WEEKS, how many whole days of school have you missed...

    C18b: Because you skipped or "cut"

     1. None
     2. 1 day
     3. 2 days
     4. 3 days
     5. 4-5 days
     6. 6-10 days
     7. 11 or more

V178   **902C19 :#DA/4W SKP CLASS**   **REF 13**
         MISSING -9

       C19: During the last four weeks, how often have you gone to school, but skipped a class

       when you weren't supposed to?

     1. Not at all
     2. 1 or 2 times
     3. 3-5 times
     4. 6-10 times
     5. 11-20 times
     6. More than 20 times

V179   **902C20 :R HS GRADE/D=1**   **REF 14**
         MISSING -9

       C20: Which of the following best describes your average grade so far in high school?

     9. A (93-100)
     8. A- (90-92)
     7. B+ (87-89)
     6. B (83-86)
     5. B- (80-82)
     4. C+ (77-79)
     3. C (73-76)
     2. C- (70-72)
     1. D (69 or below)

V180   **902C21A:R WL DO VOC/TEC**   **REF 15**
              MISSING -9
C21: How likely is it that you will do each of the
following things after high school?

C21a: Attend a technical or vocational school
1. Definitely won't
2. Probably won't
3. Probably will
4. Definitely will

V181   **902C21B:R WL DO ARMD FC**   **REF 16**
              MISSING -9
<See Q. C21 for complete question text.>
C21b: Serve in the armed forces
1. Definitely won't
2. Probably won't
3. Probably will
4. Definitely will

V182   **902C21C:R WL DO 2YR CLG**   **REF 17**
              MISSING -9
<See Q. C21 for complete question text.>
C21c: Graduate from a two-year college program
1. Definitely won't
2. Probably won't
3. Probably will
4. Definitely will

V183   **902C21D:R WL DO 4YR CLG**   **REF 18**
              MISSING -9
<See Q. C21 for complete question text.>
C21d: Graduate from 4-year college
1. Definitely won't
2. Probably won't
3. Probably will
4. Definitely will

V184   **902C21E:R WL DO GRD/PRF**   **REF 19**
              MISSING -9
<See Q. C21 for complete question text.>
C21e: Attend graduate or professional school after college
1. Definitely won't
2. Probably won't
3. Probably will
4. Definitely will

V191   **902C23 :HRS/W WRK SCHYR**   **REF 20**
          MISSING -9
C23: On the average over the school year, how many hours per week do you work
in a paid or unpaid job?
1. None
2. 5 or less hours
3. 6 to 10 hours
4. 11 to 15 hours
5. 16 to 20 hours
6. 21 to 25 hours
7. 26 to 30 hours
8. More than 30 hours

V192   **902C24A:R$/AVG WEEK JOB**   **REF 21**
          MISSING -9
C24: During an average week, how much money do you get from...
C24a: A job or other work
1. None
2. $1-5
3. $6-10
4. $11-20
5. $21-35
6. $36-50
7. $51-75
8. $76-125
9. $126+

V193   **902C24B:R$/AVG WEEK OTH**   **REF 22**
          MISSING -9
<See Q. C24 for complete question text.>
C24b: Other sources (allowances, etc.)
1. None
2. $1-5
3. $6-10
4. $11-20
5. $21-35
6. $36-50
7. $51-75
8. $76-125
9. $126+

V194   902C25 :#X/AV WK GO OUT   REF 23
          MISSING -9

     C25: During a typical week, on how many evenings do you go out for fun and
recreation?
          1. Less than one
          2. One
          3. Two
          4. Three
          5. Four or five
          6. Six or seven

V195   902C26 :#X DATE 3+/WK   REF 24
          MISSING -9

     C26: On the average, how often do you go out with a date (or your spouse, if you
are
          married)?
          1. Never
          2. Once a month or less
          3. 2 or 3 times a month
          4. Once a week
          5. 2 or 3 times a week
          6. Over 3 times a week

V196   902C27 :DRIVE>200 MI/WK   REF 25
          MISSING -9

     C27: During an average week, how much do you usually drive a car, truck, or
motorcycle?
          1. Not at all
          2. 1 to 10 miles
          3. 11 to 50 miles
          4. 51 to 100 miles
          5. 100 to 200 miles
          6. More than 200 miles

V197   902C28 :#X/12MO R TCKTD   REF 26
          MISSING -9

     C28: Within the LAST 12 MONTHS, how many times, if any, have you received a
ticket (OR been stopped and warned) for moving violations, such as speeding, running a
stop light, or improper passing?
          0. None--GO TO Q. C30
          1. Once
          2. Twice
          3. Three times
          4. Four or more times

V101   902B01 :EVR SMK CIG,REGL   REF 27
          MISSING -9
     B01: Have you ever smoked cigarettes?
          1. Never--Go to Question B03
          2. Once or twice
          3. Occasionally but not regularly
          4. Regularly in the past
          5. Regularly now

V103   902B03 :EVER DRINK   REF 28
          MISSING -9
     B03: Next we want to ask you about drinking alcoholic beverages, including beer,
wine, wine coolers, and liquor.

     Have you ever had any beer, wine, wine coolers, or liquor to drink?
          1. No--Go to Q. B07
          2. Yes

V104   902B04A:#X DRNK/LIFETIME   REF 29
          MISSING -9
     B04: On how many occasions have you had alcoholic beverages to drink...

     B04a: Alcohol in your lifetime?
          1. 0 occasions (includes 1. in B03)
          2. 1-2
          3. 3-5
          4. 6-9
          5. 10-19
          6. 20-39
          7. 40 or more

V106   902B04C:#X DRNK/LAST30DA   REF 30
          MISSING -9
     <See Q. B04 for complete question text.>
     B04c: Alcohol during the last 30 days?
          1. 0 occasions (includes 1. in B03)
          2. 1-2
          3. 3-5
          4. 6-9
          5. 10-19
          6. 20-39
          7. 40 or more

V107   902B05 :#X DRK ENF FL HI   REF 31
MISSING -9

B05: On the occasions that you drink alcoholic beverages, how often do you drink enough to feel pretty high?
1. On none of the occasions
2. On few of the occasions
3. On about half of the occasions
4. On most of the occasions
5. On nearly all of the occasions

V108   902B06 :5+DRK ROW/LST 2W   REF 32
MISSING -9

B06: Think back over the LAST TWO WEEKS. How many times have you had five or more drinks in a row? (A "drink" is a bottle of beer, a glass of wine, a wine cooler, a shot glass of liquor, or a mixed drink.)
1. None (includes 1. in B03)
2. Once
3. Twice
4. Three to five times
5. Six to nine times
6. Ten or more times

THE NEXT MAJOR SECTION OF THIS QUESTIONNAIRE DEALS WITH VARIOUS OTHER DRUGS. THERE IS A LOT OF TALK THESE DAYS ABOUT THIS SUBJECT, BUT VERY LITTLE ACCURATE INFORMATION.

THEREFORE, WE STILL HAVE A LOT TO LEARN ABOUT THE ACTUAL EXPERIENCES AND ATTITUDES OF PEOPLE YOUR AGE.

WE HOPE THAT YOU CAN ANSWER ALL QUESTIONS; BUT IF YOU FIND ONE WHICH YOU FEEL YOU CANNOT ANSWER HONESTLY, WE WOULD PREFER THAT YOU LEAVE IT BLANK.

REMEMBER THAT YOUR ANSWERS WILL BE KEPT STRICTLY CONFIDENTIAL: THEY ARE NEVER CONNECTED WITH YOUR NAME OR YOUR CLASS.

V115   902B07A:#XMJ+HS/LIFETIME   REF 33
        MISSING -9

B07: On how many occasions (if any) have you used marijuana (grass, pot) or hashish (hash, hash oil)...

  B07a: Marijuana/hashish in your lifetime?
     1. 0 occasions
     2. 1-2
     3. 3-5
     4. 6-9
     5. 10-19
     6. 20-39
     7. 40 or more

V117   902B07C:#XMJ+HS/LAST30DA   REF 34
        MISSING -9

<See Q. B07 for complete question text.>
B07c: Marijuana/hashish during thc last 30 days?

     1. 0 occasions
     2. 1-2
     3. 3-5
     4. 6-9
     5. 10-19
     6. 20-39
     7. 40 or more

V124   902B10A:#X COKE/LIFETIME   REF 35
        MISSING -9

B10: On how many occasions (if any) have you used cocaine...
B10a: Cocaine in your lifetime?

     1. 0 occasions
     2. 1-2
     3. 3-5
     4. 6-9
     5. 10-19
     6. 20-39
     7. 40 or more

V126   **902B10C:#X COKE/LAST30DA**   **REF 36**
        MISSING -9
<See Q. B10 for complete question text.>
B10c: Cocaine during the last 30 days?
    1. 0 occasions
    2. 1-2
    3. 3-5
    4. 6-9
    5. 10-19
    6. 20-39
    7. 40 or more

V139   **902B15A:#X 'H'/LIFETIME**   **REF 37**
        MISSING -9
B15: On how many occasions (if any) have you used heroin (smack, horse, skag)...
B15a: Heroin in your lifetime?
    1. 0 occasions
    2. 1-2
    3. 3-5
    4. 6-9
    5. 10-19
    6. 20-39
    7. 40 or more

V141   **902B15C:#X 'H'/LAST 30DA**   **REF 38**
        MISSING -9
<See Q. B15 for complete question text.>
B15c: Heroin during the last 30 days?
    1. 0 occasions
    2. 1-2
    3. 3-5
    4. 6-9
    5. 10-19
    6. 20-39
    7. 40 or more

V1643   **901A006C:SAT PRSNL SAFTY**   **REF 39**
        MISSING -9
    A06: How satisfied are you with...
<See Q. A06 for complete question text.>
    A06c: Your personal safety in your neighborhood, on your job, and in your
school—safety from being attacked and injured in some way?
    7. Completely satisfied
    6. .
    5. .

4. Neutral

3. .

2. .

1. Completely dissatisfied

V1645   901A006E:SAT EDUC EXPRNC   **REF 40**
            MISSING -9
<See Q. A06 for complete question text.>
A06e: Your educational experiences?

7. Completely satisfied

6. .

5. .

4. Neutral

3. .

2. .

1. Completely dissatisfied

V1646   901A006F:SAT OWN FRIENDS   **REF 41**
            MISSING -9
<See Q. A06 for complete question text.>
A06f: Your friends and other people you spend time with?

7. Completely satisfied

6. .

5. .

4. Neutral

3. .

2. .

1. Completely dissatisfied

V1647   901A006G:SAT GT ALNG PRN   **REF 42**
            MISSING -9
<See Q. A06 for complete question text.>
A06g: The way you get along with your parents?

7. Completely satisfied

6. .

5. .

4. Neutral

3. .

2. .

1. Completely dissatisfied

V1648 **901A006H:SAT YOURSELF** **REF 43**
MISSING -9
<See Q. A06 for complete question text.>
A06h: Yourself?
  7. Completely satisfied
  6. .
  5. .
  4. Neutral
  3. .
  2. .
  1. Completely dissatisfied

V1652 **901A006L:SAT LIFE AS WHL** **REF 44**
MISSING -9
<See Q. A06 for complete question text.>
A06l: Your life as a whole these days?
  7. Completely satisfied
  6. .
  5. .
  4. Neutral
  3. .
  2. .
  1. Completely dissatisfied

V1653 **901A006M:SAT GOVT OPRTNG** **REF 45**
MISSING -9
<See Q. A06 for complete question text.>
A06m: The way our national government is operating?

  7. Completely satisfied
  6. .
  5. .
  4. Neutral
  3. .
  2. .
  1. Completely dissatisfied

V1654 **901A006N:SAT AMT OF FUN** **REF 46**
MISSING -9
<See Q. A06 for complete question text.>
A06n: The amount of fun you are having?
  7. Completely satisfied
  6. .
  5. .
  4. Neutral
  3. .

2. .
  1. Completely dissatisfied

V1655   901A007A:IMP B SUCCSS WK   REF 47
  MISSING -9
A07: How important is each of the following to you in your life?
A07a: Being successful in my line of work
  1. Not important
  2. Somewhat important
  3. Quite important
  4. Extremely important

V1656   901A007B:IMP GD MRRG&FAM   REF 48
  MISSING -9
<See Q. A07 for complete question text.>
A07b: Having a good marriage and family life
  1. Not important
  2. Somewhat important
  3. Quite important
  4. Extremely important

V1657   901A007C:IMP LOTS OF $ REF 49
  MISSING -9
<See Q. A07 for complete question text.>
A07c: Having lots of money
  1. Not important
  2. Somewhat important
  3. Quite important
  4. Extremely important

V1658   901A007D:IMP TM RCRN&HBY   REF 50
  MISSING -9
<See Q. A07 for complete question text.>
A07d: Having plenty of time for recreation and hobbies
  1. Not important
  2. Somewhat important
  3. Quite important
  4. Extremely important

V1659   901A007E:IMP STRG FRDSHP   **REF 51**
MISSING -9
<See Q. A07 for complete question text.>
A07e: Having strong friendships
1. Not important
2. Somewhat important
3. Quite important
4. Extremely important

V1660   901A007F:IMP STEADY WORK   **REF 52**
MISSING -9
<See Q. A07 for complete question text.>
A07f: Being able to find steady work
1. Not important
2. Somewhat important
3. Quite important
4. Extremely important

V1661   901A007G:IMP CNTRBTN SOC   **REF 53**
MISSING -9
<See Q. A07 for complete question text.>
A07g: Making a contribution to society
1. Not important
2. Somewhat important
3. Quite important
4. Extremely important

V1662   901A007H:IMP LDR COMUNTY   **REF 54**
MISSING -9
<See Q. A07 for complete question text.>
A07h: Being a leader in my community
1. Not important
2. Somewhat important
3. Quite important
4. Extremely important

V1663   901A007I:IMP CHLD BTR OP   **REF 55**
MISSING -9
<See Q. A07 for complete question text.>
A07i: Being able to give my children better opportunities than I've had
1. Not important
2. Somewhat important
3. Quite important
4. Extremely important

V1666   901A007L:IMP CRRCT INEQL   REF 56
MISSING -9
<See Q. A07 for complete question text.>
A07l: Working to correct social and economic inequalities
   1. Not important
   2. Somewhat important
   3. Quite important
   4. Extremely important

V1669   901A008 :PPL CAN B TRSTD   REF 57
MISSING -9
A08: Generally speaking, would you say that most people can be trusted or that you can't be too careful in dealing with people?
   3. Most people can be trusted
   2. Don't know, undecided
   1. Can't be too careful

V1670   901A009 :PPL TRY B HLPFL   REF 58
MISSING -9
A09: Would you say that most of the time people try to be helpful or that they are mostly just looking out for themselves?
   3. Try to be helpful
   2. Don't know, undecided
   1. Just looking out for themselves
   2.

V1671   901A010 :PPL TRY BE FAIR   REF 59
MISSING -9
A10: Do you think most people would try to take advantage of you if they got a chance or would they try to be fair?
   3. Would try to be fair
   2. Don't know, undecided
   1. Would try to take advantage of you

V1672   901A011A:-OBY LW=-GD CTZ   REF 60
MISSING -9
A11: These next questions ask your opinions about a number of different topics. How much do you agree or disagree with each statement below?

A11a: I feel that you can't be a good citizen unless you always obey the law
   1. Disagree
   2. Mostly disagree
   3. Neither
   4. Mostly agree
   5. Agree

V1673   901A011B:GD CTZN ALG GOV   REF 61
              MISSING –9
<See Q. A11 for complete question text.>
A11b: I feel a good citizen should go along with whatever the government does even if he disagrees with it
    1. Disagree
    2. Mostly disagree
    3. Neither
    4. Mostly agree
    5. Agree

V1674   901A011C:GD CTZN CHG GOV   REF 62
          MISSING -9
  <See Q. A11 for complete question text.>
  A11c: I feel a good citizen tries to change the government policies he disagrees with
    1. Disagree
    2. Mostly disagree
    3. Neither
    4. Mostly agree
    5. Agree

V1766   901A012A:RSK OF CIG1+PK/   REF 63
              MISSING -9
 A12: The next questions ask for your opinions on the effects of using certain drugs and other substances. How much do you think people risk harming themselves (physically or in other ways), if they...

  A12a: Smoke one or more packs of cigarettes per day
    1. No risk
    2. Slight risk
    3. Moderate risk
    4. Great risk

V1767   901A012B:RSK OF MJ 1-2 X   REF 64
              MISSING -9
  <See Q. A12 for complete question text.>
  A12b: Try marijuana once or twice
    1. No risk
    2. Slight risk
    3. Moderate risk
    4. Great risk

V1770   901A012E:RSK COK PWDR 1-   **REF 65**
MISSING -9
<See Q. A12 for complete question text.>
A12e: Try cocaine in powder form once or twice
1. No risk
2. Slight risk
3. Moderate risk
4. Great risk

V1773   901A012H:RSK CRACK 1-2X   **REF 66**
MISSING -9
<See Q. A12 for complete question text.>
A12h: Try "crack" cocaine once or twice
1. No risk
2. Slight risk
3. Moderate risk
4. Great risk

V1776   901A012K:RSK OF 1-2 DRIN   **REF 67**
MISSING -9
<See Q. A12 for complete question text.>
A12k: Try one or two drinks of an alcoholic beverage (beer, wine, liquor)
1. No risk
2. Slight risk
3. Moderate risk
4. Great risk

V1779   901A012N:RSK OF 5+DR/WKN   **REF 68**
MISSING -9
<See Q. A12 for complete question text.>
A12n: Have five or more drinks once or twice each weekend
1. No risk
2. Slight risk
3. Moderate risk
4. Great risk

V1780   901A013A:EASY GT MARIJUA   **REF 69**
MISSING -9
A13: How difficult do you think it would be for you to get each of the following types of drugs, if you wanted some?

A13a: Marijuana
   1. Probably impossible
   2. Very difficult
   3. Fairly difficult
   4. Fairly easy
   5. Very easy

VAR 1781   901A013B:EASY GT CRACK   REF 70
              MISSING -9
<See Q. A13 for complete question text.>
A13b: "Crack" cocaine
   1. Probably impossible
   2. Very difficult
   3. Fairly difficult
   4. Fairly easy
   5. Very easy

V1782   901A013C:EASY GT COK PWD   REF 71
              MISSING -9
<See Q. A13 for complete question text.>
A13c: Cocaine powder
   1. Probably impossible
   2. Very difficult
   3. Fairly difficult
   4. Fairly easy
   5. Very easy

THE NEXT QUESTIONS ARE ABOUT YOUR EXPERIENCES IN SCHOOL.

V1682   901D001 :R LIKES SCHOOL   REF 72
              MISSING -9
   D01: Some people like school very much. Others don't. How do you feel about going to school?
   5. I like school very much
   4. I like school quite a lot
   3. I like school some
   2. I don't like school very much
   1. I don't like school at all

V1683   **901D002 :*SC WRK NVR MNG**   **REF 73**
     MISSING -9

D02: How often do you feel that the school work you are assigned is meaningful and

     important?
     5. Almost always
     4. Often
     3. Sometimes
     2. Seldom
     1. Never

V1684   **901D003 :*MST COUR V DUL**   **REF 74**
     MISSING -9

D03: How interesting are most of your courses to you?
     5. Very exciting and stimulating
     4. Quite interesting
     3. Fairly interesting
     2. Slightly dull
     1. Very dull

V1685   **901D004 :*LRN SCH NT IMP**   **REF 75**
     MISSING -9

D04: How important do you think the things you are learning in school are going to be for your later life?
     5. Very important
     4. Quite important
     3. Fairly important
     2. Slightly important
     1. Not at all important

V1686   **901D005 :LOT CMPTN GRADE**   **REF 76**
     MISSING -9

D05: How much competition for grades is there among students at your school?
     1. None
     2. A little
     3. Some
     4. Quite a bit
     5. A great deal

V1687   901D006 :STDTS DSLK CHTG   REF 77
MISSING -9

D06: How do you think most of the students in your classes would feel if you cheated on a test?
1. They would like it very much
2. They would like it
3. They would not care
4. They would dislike it
5. They would dislike it very much

V1688   901D007 :ST -LK PROV TCH   REF 78
MISSING -9

D07: How do you think most of the students in your classes would feel if you intentionally did things to make your teachers angry?
1. They would like it very much
2. They would like it
3. They would not care
4. They would dislike it
5. They would dislike it very much

V1733   901D016A:#X/12M DOC-CHEK   REF 79
MISSING -9

D16: In the LAST 12 MONTHS, how many times (if any) have you seen a doctor or other professional for each of the following

D16a: For a routine physical check-up
1. None
2. Once
3. Twice
4. 3 to 5 times
5. 6 to 9 times
6. 10+ times

V1734   901D016B:#X/12M DOC-FGHT   REF 80
MISSING -9

<See Q. D16 for complete question text.>
D16b: For an injury suffered in a fight, assault, or auto accident
1. None
2. Once
3. Twice
4. 3 to 5 times
5. 6 to 9 times
6. 10+ times

V1735   **901D016C:#X/12M DOC-INJ**   **REF 81**
        MISSING -9
<See Q. D16 for complete question text.>
D16c: For any other accidental injury
    1. None
    2. Once
    3. Twice
    4. 3 to 5 times
    5. 6 to 9 times
    6. 10+ times

V1736   **901D016D:#X/12M DOC-ILL**   **REF 82**
        MISSING -9
<See Q. D16 for complete question text.>
D16d: For some physical illness/symptom
    1. None
    2. Once
    3. Twice
    4. 3 to 5 times
    5. 6 to 9 times
    6. 10+ times

V1740   **901D018 :RLTV PHY HEALTH**   **REF 83**
        MISSING -9
    D18: Overall, relative to other people your age, do you think your physical health
over the past year has been...
    1. Much poorer than average
    2. Somewhat poorer
    3. About average
    4. Somewhat better
    5. Much better than average

V1791   **901D021A:DAP SMK 1PCK CI**   **REF 84**
        MISSING -9
    D21: Individuals differ in whether or not they disapprove of people doing certain
things. Do YOU disapprove of people (who are 18 or older) doing each of the following.

    D21a: Smoking one or more packs of cigarettes per day
    1. Don't disapprove
    2. Disapprove
    3. Strongly disapprove

V1792   901D021B:DAP TRY MRJ 1-2   REF 85
          MISSING -9
<See Q. D21 for complete question text.>
D21b: Trying marijuana once or twice
     1. Don't disapprove
     2. Disapprove
     3. Strongly disapprove

V1795   901D021E:DAP COK PWD 1-2   REF 86
          MISSING -9
<See Q. D21 for complete question text.>
D21e: Trying cocaine in powder form once or twice
     1. Don't disapprove
     2. Disapprove
     3. Strongly disapprove

V1798   901D021H:DAP TRY CRK 1-2   REF 87
          MISSING -9
<See Q. D21 for complete question text.>
D21h: Trying "crack" cocaine once or twice
     1. Don't disapprove
     2. Disapprove
     3. Strongly disapprove

V1801   901D021K:DAP TRY DRK ALC   REF 88
          MISSING - 9
<See Q. D21 for complete question text.>
D21k: Trying one or two drinks of an alcoholic beverage (beer, wine, liquor)
     1. Don't disapprove
     2. Disapprove
     3. Strongly disapprove

V1804   901D021N:DAP 5+ DRK WKND   REF 89
          MISSING -9

<See Q. D21 for complete question text.>
D21n: Having five or more drinks once or twice each weekend
     1. Don't disapprove
     2. Disapprove
     3. Strongly disapprove

V1   **Year of Study**   **REF 90**
                     MISSING - 9
          1990.   1990
          2000.   2000

INDEX OF VARIABLE NUMBERS TO REFERENCE NUMBERS

The variable numbers in the dataset are not listed sequentially since they may come from the core or form one (one of the six forms) of the questionnaire. This list gives the variable numbers cross-listed against their reference numbers. The reference numbers are sequential for this codebook.

V13	SCHL RGN-4 CAT	REF 1
V49	# SIBLINGS	REF 4
V101	902B01 :EVR SMK CIG,REGL	REF 27
V103	902B03 :EVER DRINK	REF 28
V104	902B04A:#X DRNK/LIFETIME	REF 29
V106	902B04C:#X DRNK/LAST30DA	REF 30
V107	902B05 :#X DRK ENF FL HI	REF 31
V108	902B06 :5+DRK ROW/LST 2W	REF 32
V115	902B07A:#XMJ+HS/LIFETIME	REF 33
V117	902B07C:#XMJ+HS/LAST30DA	REF 34
V124	902B10A:#X COKE/LIFETIME	REF 35
V126	902B10C:#X COKE/LAST30DA	REF 36
V139	902B15A:#X 'H'/LIFETIME	REF 37
V141	902B15C:#X 'H'/LAST 30DA	REF 38
V150	902C03 :R'S SEX	REF 2
V151	902C04 :R'S RACE	REF 3
V163	902C08 :FATIIR EDUC LEVEL	REF 5
V164	902C09 :MOTHR EDUC LEVEL	REF 6
V166	902C11 :R'S POLTL PRFNC	REF 7
V167	902C12 :R'POL BLF RADCL	REF 8
V172	902C15 :R'S HS PROGRAM	REF 9
V173	902C16 :RT SF SCH AB>AVG	REF 10
V174	902C17 :RT SF INTELL>AVG	REF 11
V176	902C18B:#DA/4W SC MS CUT	REF 12
V178	902C19 :#DA/4W SKP CLASS	REF 13
V179	902C20 :R HS GRADE/D=1	REF 14
V180	902C21A:R WL DO VOC/TEC	REF 15
V181	902C21B:R WL DO ARMD FC	REF 16
V182	902C21C:R WL DO 2YR CLG	REF 17
V183	902C21D:R WL DO 4YR CLG	REF 18
V184	902C21E:R WL DO GRD/PRF	REF 19
V191	902C23 :HRS/W WRK SCHYR	REF 20
V192	902C24A:R$/AVG WEEK JOB	REF 21
V193	902C24B:R$/AVG WEEK OTH	REF 22

V194	902C25 :#X/AV WK GO OUT	REF 23
V195	902C26 :#X DATE 3+/WK	REF 24
V196	902C27 :DRIVE>200 MI/WK	REF 25
V197	902C28 :#X/12MO R TCKTD	REF 26
V1643	901A006C:SAT PRSNL SAFTY	REF 39
V1645	901A006E:SAT EDUC EXPRNC	REF 40
V1646	901A006F:SAT OWN FRIENDS	REF 41
V1647	901A006G:SAT GT ALNG PRN	REF 42
V1648	901A006H:SAT YOURSELF	REF 43
V1652	901A006L:SAT LIFE AS WHL	REF 44
V1653	901A006M:SAT GOVT OPRTNG	REF 45
V1654	901A006N:SAT AMT OF FUN	REF 46
V1655	901A007A:IMP B SUCCSS WK	REF 47
V1656	901A007B:IMP GD MRRG&FAM	REF 48
V1657	901A007C:IMP LOTS OF $	REF 49
V1658	901A007D:IMP TM RCRN&HBY	REF 50
V1659	901A007E:IMP STRG FRDSHP	REF 51
V1660	901A007F:IMP STEADY WORK	REF 52
V1661	901A007G:IMP CNTRBTN SOC	REF 53
V1662	901A007H:IMP LDR COMUNTY	REF 54
V1663	901A007I:IMP CHLD BTR OP	REF 55
V1666	901A007L:IMP CRRCT INEQL	REF 56
V1669	901A008 :PPL CAN B TRSTD	REF 57
V1670	901A009 :PPL TRY B HLPFL	REF 58
V1671	901A010 :PPL TRY BE FAIR	REF 59
V1672	901A011A:-OBY LW=-GD CTZ	REF 60
V1673	901A011B:GD CTZN ALG GOV	REF 61
V1674	901A011C:GD CTZN CHG GOV	REF 62
V1682	901D001 :R LIKES SCHOOL	REF 72
V1683	901D002 :*SC WRK NVR MNG	REF 73
V1684	901D003 :*MST COUR V DUL	REF 74
V1685	901D004 :*LRN SCH NT IMP	REF 75
V1686	901D005 :LOT CMPTN GRADE	REF 76
V1687	901D006 :STDTS DSLK CHTG	REF 77
V1688	901D007 :ST -LK PROV TCH	REF 78
V1733	901D016A:#X/12M DOC-CHEK	REF 79
V1734	901D016B:#X/12M DOC-FGHT	REF 80
V1735	901D016C:#X/12M DOC-INJ	REF 81
V1736	901D016D:#X/12M DOC-ILL	REF 82
V1740	901D018 :RLTV PHY HEALTH	REF 83
V1766	901A012A:RSK OF CIG1+PK/	REF 63
V1767	901A012B:RSK OF MJ 1-2 X	REF 64
V1770	901A012E:RSK COK PWDR 1-	REF 65
V1773	901A012H:RSK CRACK 1-2X	REF 66
V1776	901A012K:RSK OF 1-2 DRIN	REF 67
V1779	901A012N:RSK OF 5+DR/WKN	REF 68

V1780	901A013A:EASY GT MARIJUA	REF 69
V1781	901A013B:EASY GT CRACK	REF 70
V1782	901A013C:EASY GT COK PWD	REF 71
V1791	901D021A:DAP SMK 1PCK CI	REF 84
V1792	901D021B:DAP TRY MRJ 1-2	REF 85
V1795	901D021E:DAP COK PWD 1-2	REF 86
V1798	901D021H:DAP TRY CRK 1-2	REF 87
V1801	901D021K:DAP TRY DRK ALC	REF 88
V1804	901D021N:DAP 5+ DRK WKND	REF 89
V1	Year of Study	REF 90

INSTRUCTIONAL CODEBOOK
FOR
NATIONAL OPINION SURVEY OF CRIME AND JUSTICE, 1995

PART 2: NATIONAL DATA

(ICPSR 6720)

Flanagan, Timothy J., and Dennis R. Longmire. NATIONAL OPINION SURVEY
OF CRIME AND JUSTICE, 1995. ICPSR version. Huntsville, TX: Sam Houston
State University, Criminal Justice Center, Survey Research Program [producer], 1995.
 Ann Arbor, MI: Inter-university Consortium for Political and Social Research
[distributor], 1996.

PREFACE

This data was collected by Timothy J. Flanagan and Dennis R. Longmire
(Principal Investigators) as a survey to provide legislators, public officials, and researchers
in Texas with a reliable source of information about citizen attitudes and opinions about
crime. The data collection consists of two distinctly different files, National Data (Part 2)
and Texas data (Part 1), which can be linked or used separately for analysis.

This workbook includes a subset of variables from the National datafile. The
sampling universe was all individuals in the continental United States with a telephone in
their residence. The survey employed a random sampling design. The response rates were
64% in Texas and 65% in the Nation.

A detailed explanation of how to read this codebook is provided in Chapter 1 of this
workbook.

These data were originally weighted to reflect sampling design. Thus, results from
the instructional data file may differ from the original data collection.

The instructional datafile in SPSS © format is named:

Noscj95.sav

SAM HOUSTON STATE UNIVERSITY
NATIONAL CRIME & JUSTICE SURVEY

Hello, this is _____calling from the Public Policy Research Institute at Texas A & M University. We are conducting a nationwide survey of people's opinions about crime and justice in America. May I speak with the man or lady of the household who is 18 years of age or older who had the most recent birthday? (if under 18 then terminate)

M1 First of all, I would like to get your opinions about issues dealing with crime and justice in America. Concerning media coverage of crime, how much attention does the local media in your community give to violent crime? Would you say it is: too much, too little or about right? **(REF 1)**
- 1 Too much
- 2 About right
- 3 Too little
- M 8 Don't know
- M 9 Refused

M2 Do you get most of your news about crime from television, newspapers, radio, co-workers or friends and neighbors? **(REF 2)**
- 1 Television
- 2 Newspapers
- 3 Radio
- 4 Co-workers
- 5 Friends and neighbors
- 6 Other, specify _____
- M 8 Don't know
- M 9 Refused

M3 Are you a regular viewer of television programs that deal with crime or criminal justice issues, such as COPS, Real Stories of the Highway Patrol, Justice Files or America's Most Wanted? **(REF 3)**
- 1 Yes
- 2 No
- M 8 Don't know
- M 9 Refused

M4 Approximately how many hours do you watch television per week? (record exact response) **(REF 4)**

_____
- M 888 Don't know
- M 999 Refused

Changing topics, I would like to ask you about various aspects of your neighborhood. For each of the following would you say it is a serious problem, somewhat of a problem, a minor problem or not a problem at all?

 N1 Trash and litter lying around (**REF 5**)

   1 Serious problem
   2 Somewhat of a problem
   3 A minor problem
   4 Not a problem at all
 M 8 Don't know
 M 9 Refused

 N2 Neighborhood dogs running loose (**REF 6**)
   1 Serious problem
   2 Somewhat of a problem
   3 A minor problem
   4 Not a problem at all
 M 8 Don't know
 M 9 Refused

 N3 Graffiti on sidewalks and walls (**REF 7**)
   1 Serious problem
   2 Somewhat of a problem
   3 A minor problem
   4 Not a problem at all
 M 8 Don't know
 M 9 Refused

 N4 Vacant houses and unkempt lots (**REF 8**)
   1 Serious problem
   2 Somewhat of a problem
   3 A minor problem
   4 Not a problem at all
 M 8 Don't know
 M 9 Refused

 N5 Unsupervised youth (**REF 9**)
   1 Serious problem
   2 Somewhat of a problem
   3 A minor problem
   4 Not a problem at all
 M 8 Don't know
 M 9 Refused

N6 Too much noise (**REF 10**)
    1 Serious problem
    2 Somewhat of a problem
    3 A minor problem
    4 Not a problem at all
M 8 Don't know
M 9 Refused

N7 People drunk or high on drugs in public (**REF 11**)
    1 Serious problem
    2 Somewhat of a problem
    3 A minor problem
    4 Not a problem at all
M 8 Don't know
M 9 Refused

N8 Abandoned cars or car parts lying around (**REF 12**)
    1 Serious problem
    2 Somewhat of a problem
    3 A minor problem
    4 Not a problem at all
M 8 Don't know
M 9 Refused

N9 In the past year do you feel that the crime rate in your neighborhood has increased, decreased or stayed the same? (**REF 13**)
    1 Increased
    2 Stayed the same
    3 Decreased
M 8 Don't know
M 9 Refused

N10 In the past year do you feel safer, not as safe or about the same on the streets in your neighborhood? (**REF 14**)
    1 Safer
    2 Not as safe
    3 About the same
M 8 Don't know
M 9 Refused

Next, I want to ask you how much you worry about each of the following situations. Do you worry very frequently, somewhat frequently, seldom or never about:

W1 Yourself or someone in your family getting sexually assaulted (**REF 15**)
    1   Very frequently
    2   Somewhat frequently
    3   Seldom
    4   Never
M   8   Don't know
M   9   Refused

W2 Being attacked while driving your car (**REF 16**)
    1   Very frequently
    2   Somewhat frequently
    3   Seldom
    4   Never
M   8   Don't know
M   9   Refused

W3 Getting mugged (**REF 17**)
    1   Very frequently
    2   Somewhat frequently
    3   Seldom
    4   Never
M   8   Don't know
M   9   Refused

W4 Getting beaten up, knifed or shot (**REF 18**)
    1   Very frequently
    2   Somewhat frequently
    3   Seldom
    4   Never
M   8   Don't know
M   9   Refused

W5 Getting murdered   (**REF 19**)
    1   Very frequently
    2   Somewhat frequently
    3   Seldom
    4   Never
M   8   Don't know
M   9   Refused

W6 Your home being burglarized while someone is at home (**REF 20**)
    1   Very frequently
    2   Somewhat frequently

     3   Seldom
     4   Never
M   8   Don't know
M   9   Refused

W7 Your home being burglarized while no one is at home   **(REF 21)**
     1   Very frequently
     2   Somewhat frequently
     3   Seldom
     4   Never
M   8   Don't know
M   9   Refused

Moving to another topic, I would like to ask your opinions of the courts in your community. Do you think each of the following items are a serious problem, somewhat of a problem, a minor problem or not a problem at all in your community?

C12 In general, do you think courts in this area deal too harshly, not harshly enough or about right with criminals?   **(REF 22)**
     1   Too harshly
     2   About right
     3   Not harshly enough
M 8   Don't know
M 9   Refused

C13 Thinking now about drunk drivers, does the criminal justice system deal too harshly, not harshly enough or about right with drunk drivers? **(REF 23)**
     1   Too harshly
     2   Not harshly enough
     3   About right
M 8   Don't know
M 9   Refused

C14 In your opinion what is the most appropriate sentence for a person convicted more than once for drunk driving? (read choices 1-5) **(REF 24)**
     1   License revoked
     2   A $ 1,000 fine
     3   Community service sentence
     4   One year in jail
     5   A prison term of more than one year
M 8   Don't know
M 9   Refused

Next, people have said there are four purposes of criminal penalties. These are:
1. To discourage others from committing crimes.
2. To separate offenders from society.
3. To train, educate and counsel offenders.
4. To give offenders the punishment they deserve.

A1 Please tell me which of these four purposes do you think should be the most important in sentencing adults? (INTERVIEWERS: Note that you may need to repeat the four purposes) **(REF 25)**

    1   To discourage others from committing crimes
    2   To separate offenders from society
    3   To train, educate and counsel offenders
    4   To give offenders the punishment they deserve
M 8   Don't know
M 9   Refused

A2 Which of these four purposes do you think should be the most important in sentencing juveniles? **(REF 26)**

    1   To discourage others from committing crimes
    2   To separate offenders from society
    3   To train, educate and counsel offenders
    4   To give offenders the punishment they deserve
M 8   Don't know
M 9   Refused

A3 In recent years, some legislatures have made imprisonment mandatory for convictions for some types of crimes. Do you think these mandatory sentences are a good idea, or should judges be able to decide who goes to prison and who doesn't? **(REF 27)**

    1   Mandatory sentences are a good idea
    2   Judges should be able to decide
    3   Both
    4   Neither
M 8   Don't know
M 9   Refused

CP1 In moving on to another topic, do you favor or oppose the death penalty for persons convicted of murder? **(REF 28)**

    1   Favor
    2   Oppose
    3   Neither favor nor oppose
M 8   Don't know
M 9   Refused

I am going to read a list of items that affect some people's attitudes towards the death penalty. For each item please tell me if you would be more likely to favor the death penalty, more likely to oppose the death penalty or wouldn't matter.   For example, if it is true that:

CP2 The death penalty is not a deterrent to murder. (**REF 29**)
  1 More likely to favor
  2 Wouldn't matter
  3 More likely to oppose
 M 8 Don't know
 M 9 Refused

CP6 If it is true that: a life sentence, without any possibility of parole, was available. (**REF 30**)
  1 More likely to favor
  2 Wouldn't matter
  3 More likely to oppose
 M 8 Don't know
 M 9 Refused

CP9 If it is true that: the murderer is severely mentally retarded. (**REF 31**)
  1 More likely to favor
  2 Wouldn't matter
  3 More likely to oppose
 M 8 Don't know
 M 9 Refused

S1 Changing topics, there has been a great deal of public debate about whether marijuana use should be legal Which one of the following policies would you favor? (**REF 32**)
  (read choices 1-4)
  1 Using marijuana should be entirely legal
  2 It should be available by prescription for medical
   purposes
  3 It should be a minor violation like a parking
   ticket, but not a crime
  4 It should be a crime
 M 8 Don't know
 M 9 Refused

S2 If it were legal for people to use marijuana, should it also be legal to sell marijuana? (**REF 33**)
  1 Yes
  2 No
 M 8 Don't know
 M 9 Refused

S3   Which of the following do you think will do more to reduce the use of illegal drugs: punishing drug users or putting them into drug treatment programs?   (**REF 34**)
>   1   Punishing drug users
>   2   Putting them into drug treatment programs
>   3   Both
>   4   Neither
> M 8   Don't know
> M 9   Refused

S4   Which of the following approaches to dealing with drug use in American society do you think would be most effective? (read choices 1-4) (**REF 35**)
>   1   Military control to stop the shipping of drugs
>   across American borders
>   2   Police efforts to get drugs off American streets
>   3   Educational programs to reduce the number of drug
>   users in society
>   4   Drug treatment programs to reduce the number of
>   drug users in society
> M 8   Don't know
> M 9   Refused

S5   Which approach do you think would be least effective? (read if necessary) (**REF 36**)
>   1   Military control to stop the shipping of drugs
>   across American borders
>   2   Police efforts to get drugs off American streets
>   3   Educational programs to reduce the number of drug
>   users in society
>   4   Drug treatment programs to reduce the number of
>   drug users in society
> M 8   Don't know
> M 9   Refused

S6   From what you can tell in your community, has the government's most recent war on drugs: (read choices 1-3) (**REF 37**)
>   1   Reduced the amount of drug use
>   2   Increased the amount of drug use
>   3   Had no effect on the amount of drug use
>   8   Don't know
>   9   Refused

S7   Would you support legislation that prohibited the depiction of the use of marijuana or other illicit drugs in the movies, television or music videos? (**REF 38**)
>   1   Yes
>   2   No
> M 8   Don't know
> M 9   Refused

D1   Finally, I would like to ask you some questions about yourself. What is your current age?   (**REF 39**)
   (record exact number; range 18 to 89)

   _____

M 98 Don't know
M 99 Refused

D2   Which of the following best describes your racial or ethnic group? (read list) (**REF 40**)
   1   White
   2   Hispanic
   3   African-American
   4   Other, specify _____
M 8   Don't know
M 9   Refused

D3   What was the last grade of school you completed? (do not read)   (**REF 41**)
   1   Grade 0-4
   2   Grade 5-8
   3   Grade 9-11, some high school
   4   Grade 12, high school graduate
   5   Grade 13-15, some college, business or trade
      school
   6   Grade 16, college graduate
   7   Graduate work
M 8   Don't know
M 9   Refused

D4   Are you currently married, widowed, divorced, separated or have you never been married? (**REF 42**)
   1   Married
   2   Widowed
   3   Divorced
   4   Separated
   5   Never married
M 8   Don't know
M 9   Refused

D6 Generally speaking, do you usually think of yourself as a Republican, Democrat, Independent or other? (**REF 43**)

    1   Republican
    2   Democrat
    3   Independent
M   4   Other, specify _____
M   8   Don't know
M   9   Refused

D7 Overall, do you consider yourself liberal, middle of the road or conservative? (**REF 44**)

    1   Liberal
    2   Middle of the road
    3   Conservative
M   4   None
M   8   Don't know
M   9   Refused

D8 Which term best describes the community in which you live. Is it rural, a small town, a small city, a suburb or an urban area?   (**REF 45**)

    1   Rural
    2   Small town
    3   Small city
    4   Suburb
    5   Urban
M   8   Don't know
M   9   Refused

D11 Do you or anyone else in the household own any guns? (**REF 46**)

    1   Yes
    2   No   (SKIP TO D13)
M   8   Don't know   (SKIP TO D13)
M   9   Refused   (SKIP TO D13)

D12 Is the main reason for the gun sport or protection against crime? (**REF 47**)

    1   Sport
    2   Protection against crime
    3   Both
    4   Neither
M   8   Don't know
M   9   Refused

D15 Please tell me your annual household income? (read list and record only one response) (**REF 48**)
      1   Less than $ 15,000
      2   Between $ 15,000 and $ 30,000
      3   Between $ 30,000 and $ 60,000
      4   Over $ 60,000
  M 8   Don't know
  M 9   Refused

That completes the survey.   Thank you for your cooperation!

D16 Record the sex of the respondent   (do not read) (**REF 49**)
      1   Male
      2   Female
  M 0   Unknown

INDEX OF VARIABLE NUMBERS TO REFERENCE NUMBERS

The variable numbers in the dataset use a variety of acronyms. This list gives the acronym cross-listed against the reference number. The reference numbers are sequential for this codebook.

A1	REF 25	N2	REF 6
A2	REF 26	N3	REF 7
A3	REF 27	N4	REF 8
C12	REF 22	N5	REF 9
C13	REF 23	N6	REF 10
C14	REF 24	N7	REF 11
CP1	REF 28	N8	REF 12
CP2	REF 29	N9	REF 13
CP6	REF 30	N10	REF 14
CP9	REF 31	S1	REF 32
D1	REF 39	S2	REF 33
D2	REF 40	S3	REF 34
D3	REF 41	S4	REF 35
D4	REF 42	S5	REF 36
D6	REF 43	S6	REF 37
D7	REF 44	S7	REF 38
D8	REF 45	W1	REF 15
D11	REF 46	W2	REF 16
D12	REF 47	W3	REF 17
D15	REF 48	W4	REF 18
D16	REF 49	W5	REF 19
M1	REF 1	W6	REF 20
M2	REF 2	W7	REF 21
M3	REF 3		
M4	REF 4		
N1	REF 5		

INSTRUCTIONAL CODEBOOK

SELECTED VARIABLES
FROM

GENERAL SOCIAL SURVEY, 1998

Principal Investigators

James A. Davis, Tom W. Smith
and Peter V. Marsden

PREFACE

The following collection of data is a subset from the 1998 release of the General Social Survey (GSS) in the United States. This codebook draws selected excerpts directly from the original study. The cumulative codebook for the GSS should be consulted for the exact wording of questions.

The data (and tabulations) utilized in this booklet were made available (in part) by the Inter-university Consortium for Political and Social Research (ICPSR). The data for the GENERAL SOCIAL SURVEY, 1972-2000 were originally collected by the National Opinion Research Center (NORC). Neither the collector of the original data nor the Consortium bears any responsibility for the analyses or interpretations presented here.

DATA COLLECTION DESCRIPTION

The GENERAL SOCIAL SURVEY, 1998 which is conducted by NORC is the definitive study of public opinion in the United States. The GSS is conducted every second year. The 1998 GSS uses a double sample method (twice the size of the previous annual GSS surveys) with eight topic modules. This instructional dataset draws from the 1998a survey. The surveys are conducted bi-annually on an ongoing basis; the samples are large and nationally representative; and the subject matter is very broad, encompassing about 1000 variables per year.

The GSS is designed to explore trends in public opinion in the USA and to allow international research using two International Social Survey Program modules.

DATA COLLECTION PROCEDURES

The basic research design involves annual in-person data collections from adults. A multi-stage probability sample based on regional status and metropolitan areas, county size, and housing units is used to select respondents. The full survey includes several weighting variables to account for sampling. The instructional dataset does not use these weights. The cumulative codebook provides an extensive discussion of sampling procedures. The study is designed to be representative of the adult population in the USA.

CONTENT AREAS AND QUESTIONNAIRE DESIGN

The GSS is perhaps the most extensive collection of data on public opinion in America. Extensive research has been done on pretty much any social science topic you can name, and on how to best ask a question about the topic.

GSS WEBSITE

The National Opinion Research Center and ICPSR have developed an on-line codebook for the General Social Survey. The data for this workbook was extracted from this website and converted into an SPSS data file.

You will need to access this web-site to obtain the exact wording of some of the questions from the GSS. The codebook in this appendix provides a summary description of variables. The web-site for the cumulative codebook is shown below.

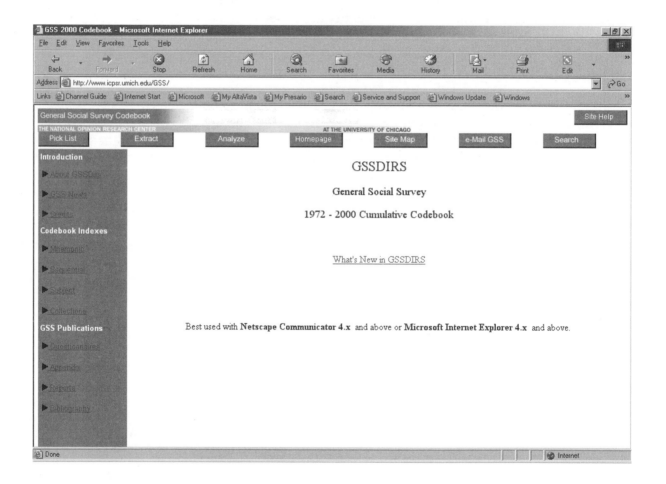

There are several methods that you can use to obtain codebook information from this site. In many instances you will simply be looking for information about a few variables. Click on the link to the Mneumonic index (on the left side of the screen) to go to an alphabetical list of mneumonic variable names.

I choose to pull up information about abortion for ABANY. The codebook provides the exact question wording, the question number(s) on the survey, and some information about frequency distributions by year of the survey.

```
Codebook Variable : ABANY - Microsoft Internet Explorer                    _ □ ×
File   Edit   View   Favorites   Tools   Help
```

Codebook Variable : ABANY

THE NATIONAL OPINION RESEARCH CENTER   AT THE UNIVERSITY OF CHICAGO

| Previous | | | Pick Page | Homepage | Pick Variable | | Next |

| Question | Links | Trends |

206. Please tell me whether or not you think it should be possible for a pregnant woman to obtain a legal abortion if...READ EACH STATEMENT, AND CIRCLE ONE CODE FOR EACH.

G. The woman wants it for any reason?

RESPONSE	PUNCH	YEAR									COL: 786
		1972-82	1982B	1983-87	1987B	1988-91	1993	1994	1996	1998	ALL
Yes	1	2221	87	2164	129	1,523	458	895	819	728	9,024
No	2	3584	237	3646	207	2,230	552	1039	1002	1050	13,547
Don't know	8	209	26	201	14	147	59	56	94	98	904
No answer	9	22	4	61	3	20	6	6	8	6	136
Not applicable	BK	7590	0	1470	0	1,987	531	996	981	950	14,505

See Appendix T, GSS Methodological Reports Nos. 19 and 42. In 1983 this question was asked immediately before Qs. 167 and 212 on Form 1. On Form 2 this question was immediately preceded by Qs. 167 and 212. See Q. 248 for a discussion of the split-half sample design. See Appendix P.

The table above shows annual frequencies for 1993, 1994, 1996, and 1998. Other years are grouped to simplify the presentation of the table. You may get the information for each individual year by using the cumulative file. This can easily be done on-line by clicking on ANALYZE on the GSS homepage.

FILE STRUCTURE

The variables described in this codebook are a subset of 49 variables from GSS 1998 Version A. They were extracted using the GSS 2000 web-site. A full description of the original data structure, files, and representative publications can be obtained from the web-site.

www.icpsr.umich.edu/GSS

The dataset is readable by the Statistical Package for the Social Sciences (SPSS © for Windows).

The instructional SPSS file is named: gss98.sav

MISSING DATA

The original data file contained several missing codes for non-response. People may refuse to answer some questions, they don't know, or a question may have been not applicable. These codes are identified as "M" in the instructional codebook.

CODEBOOK INFORMATION

The codebook available for this study was generated as an SPSS Data Dictionary using the variable and value labels provided by ICPSR in the data extraction. The questions on abortion, policing, and suicide were edited to improve the meaningfulness of the codebook for these variables. The labeling of other variables is generally clear. If you are not certain, please consult the GSS Cumulative codebook. Note that the variable names in this appendix are arranged in alphabetical order based on variable mneumonics.

File Type: SPSS Data File   gss98.sav

Total # of Defined Variable Elements: 49
Data Are Not Weighted

Variable names are in **BOLD**

Please tell me whether or not <u>you</u> think it should be possible for a pregnant woman to obtain a <u>legal</u> abortion if. . .READ EACH STATEMENT, AND CIRCLE ONE CODE FOR EACH.

ABANY   The woman wants it for any reason?
    Missing Values: 0, 8, 9
    Value   Label
      0 M NAP
      1   YES
      2   NO
      8 M DK
      9 M NA

ABRAPE   If she becomes pregnant as a result of rape?
    Missing Values: 0, 8, 9
    Value   Label
      0 M NAP
      1   YES

    2 NO
    8 M DK
    9 M NA

ABSINGLE If she is not married and does not want to marry the man?
    Missing Values: 0, 8, 9
    Value   Label
      0 M NAP
      1   YES
      2   NO
      8 M DK
      9 M NA

AGE   Age of respondent
    Missing Values: 99
    Value   Label
     98 DK
     99 M NA

CAPPUN Favor or oppose death penalty for murder
    Missing Values: 0, 8, 9
    Value   Label
      0 M NAP
      1   FAVOR
      2   OPPOSE
      8 M DK
      9 M NA

CLASS   Subjective class identification
    Missing Values: 8, 9
    Value   Label
      1   LOWER CLASS
      2   WORKING CLASS
      3   MIDDLE CLASS
      4   UPPER CLASS
      5   NO CLASS
      8 M DK
      9 M NA

CONDOM Used condom last time
    Missing Values: 8, 9
    Value   Label
      1   Yes used condom
      2   not used condom
      8 M DK
      9 M NA

DEGREE   Respondent's highest degree
    Missing Values: 7, 8, 9
    Value   Label
       0   LT HIGH SCHOOL
       1   HIGH SCHOOL
       2   JUNIOR COLLEGE
       3   BACHELOR
       4   GRADUATE
       7 M NAP
       8 M DK
       9 M NA

DWELLING Type of structure
    Missing Values: 0, 98, 99
    Value   Label
       0 M NAP
       1   TRAILER
       2   DETACHED 1-FAM HOUSE
       3   2 UNITS SIDE BY SIDE
       4   2 UNITS-ONE ABOVE
       5   3-4 FAM HOUSE
       6   ROW HOUSE
       7   APARTMENT HOUSE
       8   APARTMENT-4 STORIES
       9   APARTMENT-COMMERCIAL
      10   OTHER
     98 M DK
     99 M NA

DWELOWN   Does R own or rent home?
    Missing Values: 0, 8, 9
    Value   Label
       0 M NAP
       1   OWN OR IS BUYING
       2   PAYS RENT
       3   OTHER
       8 M DK
       9 M NA

FEAR   Afraid to walk at night in neighborhood
    Missing Values: 0, 8, 9
    Value   Label
       0 M NAP
       1   YES
       2   NO
       8 M DK

9 M NA

FEELREL How religious is R   12
  Missing Values: 0, 8, 9
  Value   Label
    1   Extreme relgious
    2   Very religious
    3   Somwhat relgious
    4   Not rel or non
    5   Somewhat non-rel
    6   Very non-rel
    7   Extreme non-rel
    8 M Cant choose
    9 M NA

GRASS   Should marijuana be made legal
  Missing Values: 0, 8, 9
  Value   Label
    0 M NAP
    1   LEGAL
    2   NOT LEGAL
    8 M DK
    9 M NA

GUNLAW   Favor or oppose gun permits
  Missing Values: 0, 8, 9
  Value   Label
    0 M NAP
    1   FAVOR
    2   OPPOSE
    8 M DK
    9 M NA

HEALTH Condition of health
  Missing Values: 0, 8, 9
  Value   Label
    0 M NAP
    1   EXCELLENT
    2   GOOD
    3   FAIR
    4   POOR
    8 M DK
    9 M NA

HUNT   Does R or spouse hunt
      Missing Values: 0, 9
      Value   Label
        0 M NAP
        1   RESP
        2   SPOUSE
        3   BOTH
        4   NEITHER
        8   DK
        9 M NA

INCOME98   Total family income
      Missing Values: 24, 98, 99
      Value   Label
        1   UNDER $1 000
        2    $1 000 to 2 999
        3    $3 000 to 3 999
        4    $4 000 to 4 999
        5    $5 000 to 5 999
        6    $6 000 to 6 999
        7    $7 000 to 7 999
        8    $8 000 to 9 999
        9    $10000 to 12499
       10    $12500 to 14999
       11    $15000 to 17499
       12    $17500 to 19999
       13    $20000 to 22499
       14    $22500 to 24999
       15    $25000 to 29999
       16    $30000 to 34999
       17    $35000 to 39999
       18    $40000 to 49999
       19    $50000 to 59999
       20    $60000 to 74999
       21    $75000 to $89999
       22    $90000 - $109999
       23    $110000 or over
       24 M REFUSED
       98 M DK
       99 M NA

MADEG   Mothers highest degree
      Missing Values: 7, 8, 9
      Value   Label
        0   LT HIGH SCHOOL
        1   HIGH SCHOOL

        2   JUNIOR COLLEGE
        3   BACHELOR
        4   GRADUATE
        7 M NAP
        8 M DK
        9 M NA

MARITAL   Marital status
      Missing Values: 9
      Value   Label
        1   MARRIED
        2   WIDOWED
        3   DIVORCED
        4   SEPARATED
        5   NEVER MARRIED
        9 M NA

NEWS   How often does R read newspaper
      Missing Values: 0, 8, 9
      Value   Label
        0 M NAP
        1   EVERYDAY
        2   FEW TIMES A WEEK
        3   ONCE A WEEK
        4   LESS THAN ONCE WK
        5   NEVER
        8 M DK
        9 M NA

OWNGUN   Have gun in home
      Missing Values: 3, 8, 9
      Value   Label
        1   YES
        2   NO
        3 M REFUSED
        8 M DK
        9 M NA

PADEG   Fathers highest degree
      Missing Values: 7, 8, 9
      Value   Label
        0   LT HIGH SCHOOL
        1   HIGH SCHOOL
        2   JUNIOR COLLEGE
        3   BACHELOR
        4   GRADUATE
        7 M NAP

            8 M DK
            9 M NA

PARTYID   Political party affiliation
          Missing Values: 7, 8, 9
          Value   Label
            0   STRONG DEMOCRAT
            1   NOT STR DEMOCRAT
            2   IND,NEAR DEM
            3   INDEPENDENT
            4   IND,NEAR REP
            5   NOT STR REPUBLICAN
            6   STRONG REPUBLICAN
            7 M OTHER PARTY
            8 M DK
            9 M NA

Several questions about police:

Are there any situations you can imagine in which you would approve of a policeman striking an adult male citizen?

IF YES OR NOT SURE: Would you approve of a policeman striking a citizen who:

POLABUSE A. Had said vulgar and obscene things to the policeman?
          Missing Values: 0, 8, 9
          Value   Label
            0 M NAP
            1   YES
            2   NO
            8 M DK
            9 M NA

POLATTAK Was attacking the policeman with his fists?
          Missing Values: 0, 8, 9
          Value   Label
            0 M NAP
            1   YES
            2   NO
            8 M DK
            9 M NA

POLESCAP Was attempting to escape from custody?
     Missing Values: 0, 8, 9
     Value   Label
       0 M NAP
       1   YES
       2   NO
       8 M DK
       9 M NA

POLHITOK Are there any situations you can imagine in which you would approve of a policeman striking an adult male citizen?
     Missing Values: 0, 8, 9
     Value   Label
       0 M NAP
       1   YES
       2   NO
       8 M DK
       9 M NA

POLMURDR Was being questioned as a suspect in a murder case?
     Missing Values: 0, 8, 9
     Value   Label
       0 M NAP
       1   YES
       2   NO
       8 M DK
       9 M NA

POLVIEWS Think of self as liberal or conservative
     Missing Values: 0, 8, 9
     Value   Label
       0 M NAP
       1   EXTREMELY LIBERAL
       2   LIBERAL
       3   SLIGHTLY LIBERAL
       4   MODERATE
       5   SLGHTLY CONSERVATIVE
       6   CONSERVATIVE
       7   EXTRMLY CONSERVATIVE
       8 M DK
       9 M NA

PORNLAW   Feelings about pornography laws
Missing Values: 0, 8, 9
Value   Label
   0 M NAP
   1   ILLEGAL TO ALL
   2   ILLEGAL UNDER 18
   3   LEGAL
   8 M DK
   9 M NA

POSTLIFE   Belief in life after death
Missing Values: 0, 8, 9
Value   Label
   0 M NAP
   1   YES
   2   NO
   8 M DK
   9 M NA

PRAY   How often does R pray
Missing Values: 0, 8, 9
Value   Label
   0 M NAP
   1   SEVERAL TIMES A DAY
   2   ONCE A DAY
   3   SEVERAL TIMES A WEEK
   4   ONCE A WEEK
   5   LT ONCE A WEEK
   6   NEVER
   8 M DK
   9 M NA

PRAYER   Bible prayer in public schools
Missing Values: 0, 8, 9
Value   Label
   0 M NAP
   1   APPROVE
   2   DISAPPROVE
   8 M DK
   9 M NA

RACE   Race of respondent
Value   Label
   1   WHITE
   2   BLACK
   3   OTHER
REGION   Region of interview

Value   Label
- 0   NOT ASSIGNED
- 1   NEW ENGLAND
- 2   MIDDLE ATLANTIC
- 3   E. NOR. CENTRAL
- 4   W. NOR. CENTRAL
- 5   SOUTH ATLANTIC
- 6   E. SOU. CENTRAL
- 7   W. SOU. CENTRAL
- 8   MOUNTAIN
- 9   PACIFIC

RELIG   Rs religious preference
Missing Values: 0, 98, 99
Value   Label
- 0 M NAP
- 1   Protestant
- 2   Catholic
- 3   Jewish
- 4   None
- 5   OTHER (SPECIFY)
- 6   BUDDHISM
- 7   HINDUISM
- 8   OTHER EASTERN
- 9   MOSLEM/ISLAM
- 10   Orthodox-christian
- 11   Chrsitian
- 12   NATIVE AMERICAN
- 13   INTER-NONDENOMINATIONAL
- 98 M DK
- 99 M NA

RINCOM98 Respondents income
Missing Values: 24, 98, 99
Value   Label
- 1   UNDER $1 000
- 2 $1 000 to 2 999
- 3 $3 000 to 3 999
- 4 $4 000 to 4 999
- 5 $5 000 to 5 999
- 6 $6 000 to 6 999
- 7 $7 000 to 7 999
- 8 $8 000 to 9 999
- 9 $10000 to 12499
- 10 $12500 to 14999
- 11 $15000 to 17499
- 12 $17500 to 19999

13   $20000 to 22499
14   $22500 to 24999
15   $25000 to 29999
16   $30000 to 34999
17   $35000 to 39999
18   $40000 to 49999
19   $50000 to 59999
20   $60000 to 74999
21   $75000 - $89999
22   $90000- $109999
23   $110 000 over
24 M REFUSED
98 M DK
99 M NA

SEX   Respondents sex
    Value   Label
     1   MALE
     2   FEMALE

SEXFREQ   Frequency of sex during last year
    Missing Values: 8, 9
    Value   Label
     0   Not at all
     1   Once or twice
     2   About once/month
     3   2-3 times/month
     4   About once/week
     5   2-3 times a week
     6   4-more times/wk
     8 M DK
     9 M NA

SOCBAR   Spend evening at bar
    Missing Values: -1, 8, 9
    Value   Label
     1   ALMOST DAILY
     2   SEV TIMES A WEEK
     3   SEV TIMES A MNTH
     4   ONCE A MONTH
     5   SEV TIMES A YEAR
     6   ONCE A YEAR
     7   NEVER
     8 M DK
     9 M NA
    -1 M NAP

SOCFREND Spend evening with friends
  Missing Values: -1, 8, 9
  Value   Label
    1   ALMOST DAILY
    2   SEV TIMES A WEEK
    3   SEV TIMES A MNTH
    4   ONCE A MONTH
    5   SEV TIMES A YEAR
    6   ONCE A YEAR
    7   NEVER
    8 M DK
    9 M NA
    -1 M NAP

SOCOMMUN Spend evening with neighbor
  Missing Values: -1, 8, 9
  Value   Label
    1   ALMOST DAILY
    2   SEV TIMES A WEEK
    3   SEV TIMES A MNTH
    4   ONCE A MONTH
    5   SEV TIMES A YEAR
    6   ONCE A YEAR
    7   NEVER
    8 M DK
    9 M NA
    -1 M NAP

SOCREL   Spend evening with relatives
  Missing Values: -1, 8, 9
  Value   Label
    1   ALMOST DAILY
    2   SEV TIMES A WEEK
    3   SEV TIMES A MNTH
    4   ONCE A MONTH
    5   SEV TIMES A YEAR
    6   ONCE A YEAR
    7   NEVER
    8 M DK
    9 M NA
    -1 M NAP

Four questions on suicide:

Do you think a person has the right to end his or her own life if this person . . .

SUICIDE1 ... has an incurable disease?
    Missing Values: 0, 8, 9
    Value   Label
      0 M NAP
      1   YES
      2   NO
      8 M DK
      9 M NA

SUICIDE2 ... has gone bankrupt?
    Missing Values: 0, 8, 9
    Value   Label
      0 M NAP
      1   YES
      2   NO
      8 M DK
      9 M NA

SUICIDE3 has dishonored his or her family?
    Missing Values: 0, 8, 9
    Value   Label
      0 M NAP
      1   YES
      2   NO
      8 M DK
      9 M NA

SUICIDE4 ... is tired of living and ready to die?
    Missing Values: 0, 8, 9
    Value   Label
      0 M NAP
      1   YES
      2   NO
      8 M DK
      9 M NA

TVHOURS Hours per day watching tv
    Missing Values: -1, 98, 99
    Value   Label
      98 M DK
      99 M NA
      -1 M NAP

XMARSEX   Sex with person other than spouse
        Missing Values: 0, 8, 9
        Value   Label
          0 M NAP
          1   ALWAYS WRONG
          2   ALMST ALWAYS WRG
          3   SOMETIMES WRONG
          4   NOT WRONG AT ALL
          5   OTHER
          8 M DK
          9 M NA